"Do you object that much?"

Flint caught Brynn's wrist and whirled her around to face him.

She gave him a pleading look. "You've got no right to kiss me at the drop of a hat. Isn't it enough that I never want to be hurt by you again?"

Sobered by a flash of raw pain in Brynn's eyes, he released her arm. "It's a bigger burden than I can live with," he replied ruefully. "The problem is that you won't forgive me." He turned to go outside, but Brynn's voice stopped him at the door.

"I'd bury the hatchet if I could, Flint."

He turned back to her. "You've got my apologies," he said gently. "Sealed with a kiss—which you reacted to with interest, I might add."

Brynn didn't respond. He knew she couldn't deny the truth of his words.

Flint smiled teasingly. "Will I get my shins kicked the next time?"

"There'd better not be a next time," she warned.

As he headed out the door, he added over his shoulder, "With me, you never know, do you?"

To Susan Sopcek
for her faith, hope and charity

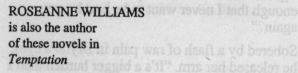

ROSEANNE WILLIAMS
is also the author
of these novels in
Temptation

THE MAGIC TOUCH
LOVE CONQUERS ALL
UNDER THE COVERS
THE BAD BOY
MAIL ORDER MAN
SEEING RED
A TRUE BLUE KNIGHT

SECOND-HAND BRIDE

BY

ROSEANNE WILLIAMS

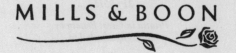

MILLS & BOON and the Rose Device are trademarks of the publisher. TEMPTATION is a trademark of Harlequin Enterprises II B.V., used under licence.
First published in Great Britain in 1995
by Harlequin Mills & Boon Limited, Eton House, 18-24 Paradise Road, Richmond, Surrey TW9 1SR

© Sheila Slattery 1995

ISBN 0 263 79494 6

21 - 9511

Printed in Great Britain by
BPC Paperbacks Ltd

1

"SACRE BLEU!"

Brynn McBride winced at her boss's explosive, angry exclamation. For the third time in three days, her work had fallen short of Armand Bergeron's expectations and her own. The short, stout Frenchman was beside himself.

"Mon dieu! What is going wrong with you this week?"

"I wish I knew," she replied miserably. "Everything I touch goes haywire."

Brynn couldn't blame him for being so exasperated with her. As the executive chef of San Francisco's premier hotel, the St. Martin, he had an outstanding culinary reputation to maintain. And as one of the chefs on his staff for the past four years, Brynn was expected to cook like a seasoned professional, not a greenhorn.

Her ragouts weren't supposed to scorch as they'd done yesterday. Her hollandaise sauce wasn't supposed to curdle as it had done time and again the day before that.

Much worse, the six cheese-asparagus soufflés she'd removed from the oven a moment ago weren't supposed to bear a revolting resemblance to road kill. Yet there they were, her very own luncheon creations, flat beyond belief.

"This is not haute cuisine!" Armand fumed. "This is—"

"The sorriest sight we've ever seen," Brynn said, interrupting to save him the trouble. "Inexcusable, unforgivable and disgraceful."

"*Oui,*" he heartily agreed. "A thousand times, *oui.* Follow me, *chérie!*"

Brynn squared her shoulders and marched behind him to his office. The sympathetic looks she got from her fellow chefs didn't help, even though each of them had, at one time or another, marched to Armand's "guillotine." It was no help, either, that Armand and his wife were two of Brynn's best friends, for friendship held no perks at all on the job.

Once in the office, Brynn sat in the hot seat in front of Armand's desk, facing him. He drummed his fingers on the desk top and bristled his dark eyebrows at her. She braced herself for her third fiery dressing-down of the week.

Surprisingly, it didn't come. Instead, Armand whooshed out a long, heavy sigh.

"What must I do now, eh? Fire you? *Non.* You have talent, too much to waste." He kept drumming his fingers. "What must I do? Make you take a vacation, yes?"

His eyebrows rose and Brynn's heart dropped to the absolute depths.

"No, please, Armand."

Brynn took pay in lieu of vacation every year, because the last thing she wanted was idle time to while away. She needed work to keep herself occupied. The busier she stayed, the less her thoughts wandered to the past, and the better off she was for it.

"Take your two weeks this year," Armand commanded. "You need a break."

Brynn grimaced. "The two days I took off last month at Christmas were enough."

Armand's brows bristled more dangerously and his dark, direct gaze threw fire. "This year I insist, for your own good."

"But Armand—"

He cut off her protest with a wave of his hand. "Your pâtés fall apart, your *coquilles* are tough." He shook his head. "My other chefs take their vacations with smiles. Do as they do, *s'il vous plaît*."

Brynn folded her arms over the front of her white chef's jacket. She crossed her knees and frowned at the traditional cross-check pattern on her chef's pants. Maybe she should never have decided to be a pro, she reflected grimly, even though she'd always had a knack for cooking.

But then, if she hadn't developed it to a professional level, she'd be what she'd been before—a dreamy, romantic, country girl who could cook but couldn't recognize a lost cause until it broke her soft, homespun heart.

Now, though, her knack wasn't living up to her own or Armand Bergeron's exacting culinary standards.

"I've let you down, Armand. And myself, too. I'm sorry."

The blaze went out of Armand's eyes. "A holiday will fix you up, *chérie*. You will return fresh and sharp two weeks from now."

"Now, in the middle of January?" Brynn gulped. "Can't it wait?" But of course it couldn't, not after her string of disasters this past week.

"Now is the best time," he replied.

Brynn couldn't dispute that, since this was truly the slowest month of the year at the St. Martin, especially in the kitchen.

"Even so, this is extremely short notice, Armand. Couldn't I just take a couple of days off, maybe?" she persisted.

He picked up a paper from his desk. "Here is my winter layoff list." Poising a fountain pen between his pudgy fingers, he inquired, "Shall I put Brynn Mc-Bride on the first line?"

"No. Don't do that." Brynn bowed to the inevitable. "Two weeks," she agreed dejectedly, "starting tomorrow. I might as well get it over with."

"*Bien*." Armand beamed an approving smile at her. "What will you do? Where will you go?"

She shrugged. "Nowhere. I'll put in more time at the shelter." She spent most of her free time cooking at the city's biggest homeless shelter, anyway.

Armand rolled his eyes and passed one hand over his perfectly bald scalp. "Brynn, you do much good for *les misérables*. Your heart is kind, but stirring the pots at the soup kitchen is not a cook's holiday."

"Time on my hands is the last thing I want. It makes me . . . think too much," Brynn confided with a sigh.

"About what, *chérie?*" Armand settled back in his chair, her friend now rather than her boss.

"Everything."

He mused, "It is much food for thought, everything."

Brynn gave him a wry smile. "You know I've stirred up a little more trouble for myself so far than the average woman my age. Married twice, divorced both times, for instance."

"Pfoof! Who is counting? Only you."

"If you were a two-time loser, you'd be counting, too. And now even my soufflés are on the skids," she added hopelessly. "Where do I go from here?"

"Home, perhaps."

Home. She pictured the sheep ranch near Bend, Oregon, where she had grown up. Armand had cooked at the neighboring guest ranch one summer before he launched his professional career in San Francisco. A year later Brynn moved to the city, on the eve of her first divorce. She enrolled in the culinary academy, graduated with honors and went straight to work for Armand at the St. Martin.

While picturing home, Brynn couldn't help thinking of Flint Wilder, the man who now owned the guest ranch where Armand had cooked for the prior owner. Since then, Armand had vacationed at the ranch several times. He knew her parents and Flint—the first of her two ex-husbands—very well.

"Home isn't my idea of a retreat, not with Flint next door," she said. "Bad idea."

"Yet you go home each Christmas," he reminded her.

"Sure, but only for two days. It's long enough to visit my parents, yet short enough to avoid Flint. In two weeks, I'd risk running into him, one way or another. No, thanks. It's over, through, finished, and I want to keep it that way."

Armand wagged a forefinger at her. "Speaking Flint's name puts *rouge* on your cheeks. You have a heart for him still, eh?"

"Crummy little leftovers," she assured Armand, if not herself. The truth was that she hadn't ever gotten over Flint and her six-month marriage to him, but she always did her best to make it seem otherwise—even to her closest friends. Her heart still broke whenever she thought of Flint Wilder. It probably always would. But nobody else had to know that. She felt foolish enough about her first marriage as it was.

Armand picked up another paper from his desk. "Flint sends me this fax letter last week. His cook is a quitter. He needs a new chef, at once, for his winter guests."

Brynn had gotten that bit of unsolicited news yesterday, in a letter from her mother, Maggie. "I'm sure he's found one by now," she replied to Armand.

"Perhaps," he said. "I have no one to recommend. Do you know of someone for him?"

"Not a soul. And if I did, I'd pretend I didn't."

"You are bitter, *petite*, yet you blush. I think you fool yourself that you can avoid Flint forever."

Brynn insisted, "I'll die trying. He'll do the same to avoid me."

Armand leveled his gaze at her. "He and you were made for each other."

"No. He and my sister were made for each other." Brynn came to her feet, upset and trying not to show how much, thinking, *Flint loved Laurel, not me. He always did and always will. He never kissed me without thinking of her. He never held me close without holding his love for her close, as well. He never made love to me without—*

She cut the painful thought short as sharp, stinging tears sprang to her eyes. "I should never have married him, Armand. Never."

Armand hastened out of his chair, clucking his tongue at himself. "I am sorry to sadden you. I should keep my big *bouche* shut about Flint, eh?"

"You should stop hoping after all this time, Armand. You and Mom and Dad."

AFTER WORK, Brynn rode a city bus to her bay-windowed, third-floor apartment on lower Nob Hill. Her two cats, Mickey and Minnie, meowed on the other side of the door as she undid the triple lock and the dead bolt.

She usually brought tidbits from the hotel kitchen for them—fish trimmings, and lobster shells to lick clean. None today, though. Her imminent vacation had made her forget their treats.

The phone started ringing the moment she walked in. Her mother.

Brynn dropped into a deep armchair with the phone in her lap. The cats sprang up onto the back of the chair,

waving their tails in her face. They loved to sniff her
hair when she came home from work, especially on the
days when Shrimp Louisiane had been the luncheon
special.

"Hi, Mom. What's new?"

"The vacation you're finally going to take."

Brynn sighed. "What did Armand do, call you the
minute I left his office?"

"No, he didn't. I phoned you at the hotel fifteen
minutes ago, thinking you'd be there after hours as
usual. He said you'd just left, and we had a chat. It's
about time you took more than a two-day breather."

"As if you've ever taken even that much time off,"
Brynn countered, visualizing her energetic mom's trim,
lively figure, short-cropped gray hair and snappy hazel eyes.

"I haven't?" Maggie sounded surprised.

Brynn said, "Face it, when you're not out tending
sheep with Dad, you're inside weaving at your loom.
Weaving wool that you personally shear, card, spin and
dye, I might add."

"Like mother, like daughter," Maggie conceded.
"Lately I've cut back on the weaving and taken up a new
craft."

"What's that?"

"Leather work. Flint is teaching me."

"Oh, er, that's . . . nice. . . ."

Brynn felt her cheeks heat again at the mention of
Flint's name. He was one of the most talented saddle
makers in the world. Custom-designed and hand-
made, his western saddles were highly prized by rodeo

champions. He'd been a champion himself, before he retired at the height of his rodeo career.

In those days, he'd been fearless, impulsive and daring. A give-'em-hell hotshot, Flint rose to the top rodeo ranks by flirting with disaster on bucking broncs and Brahma bulls.

After life at the zenith, he'd turned to cattle ranching and making saddles. His feats were now legend in the rodeo world; his saddles were becoming collectors' items.

"It's quite a challenge and I'm enjoying the craft," Maggie was saying, "not to mention the heavenly smell of fine leather. But, back to why I called—is there any chance you'll be coming home during your time off?"

Brynn hedged, "I haven't had a chance to really think about it."

"We can always use an extra pair of hands here, Brynn, if plain hard work is what you want instead of nothing to do. You know you're always as welcome as rain in a drought."

"Mom, there's plenty of work and a shortage of help at the shelter."

"We miss you, honey." Maggie's voice lowered, sounding worried. "And that's not all. Arch's ticker is acting up—artery problems, if you ask me. Stubborn old coot that he is, he won't go to the doctor or even admit anything's wrong."

Brynn's own heart lurched at Maggie's words. "Wrong? He was just fine at Christmas."

"No, Brynn. He was putting on an act, hiding every twinge. Don't tell him I said anything, though. You know Arch when he's being bullheaded."

Brynn's father had always been strong, proud and stubborn, a man to contend with. Like Flint Wilder, in a lot of ways.

"I won't breathe a word," Brynn promised, searching her startled mind for something upbeat to say. Something to ease her mother's concern, and her own, as well. "Maybe Dad just has indigestion."

"I wish, Brynn. His mother died of a heart attack, and his grandfather, too. Come home for two weeks and see for yourself what I'm talking about, hon. It isn't my imagination."

Brynn didn't need to be convinced that her salt-of-the-earth mom had a level head. "You're really worried."

"Yes, I sure am. Set aside your own worries about running into Flint. He keeps his distance anyway when he knows you're here."

Brynn pushed Flint out of her mind and started mentally packing suitcases and cat carriers. "I'll have to bring Mick and Minn. Maybe I can catch the early flight to Portland tomorrow."

"Arch and I will pick you up at the airport, hon. Phone back as soon as you know your arrival time."

BRYNN'S FLIGHT SET DOWN in an icy rainstorm at noon the next day. She hoped her parents hadn't hit deep snow passing over Mount Hood on the way to Portland. She also hoped Mick and Minn weren't freezing their whiskers off in the plane's cargo hold. This was their first trip away from home.

Brynn moved with the other passengers through the arrival gate into the air terminal, eager to see her parents. But they weren't there to greet her. She felt a sharp stab of disappointment, even though she'd anticipated all along that snow conditions on Mount Hood might delay them. Scanning the crowd of strangers in the arrival area, she puffed out a big sigh.

Then she gasped. Flint Wilder came into view as he stood up from a row of seats in the waiting area. His chiseled good looks were unmistakable: deep blue eyes, high cheekbones, square jaw and chin, black hair and eyebrows.

Brynn almost tripped on her own feet, nearly dropped her handbag, practically lost her voice except to choke out his name as he approached.

"F-Flint!"

He extended his hand to her. "Howdy, Brynn."

He had always put a mouthful of Texas twang into every word he spoke. That hadn't changed, she thought, and neither had her ex-husband. He was still a man who stood head and shoulders above most men, still a tall-in-the-saddle Texan wearing faded denims and cowboy boots.

Brynn forced a deep, steadying breath into her lungs. "What are you doing here?"

"Give a fair shake first, Brynn."

His tone was firm and direct, as she knew his grip would be if she shook hands with him. But his eyes were guarded, as if he half expected her to kick him in the shins.

"If you insist," she reluctantly agreed, giving him a handshake so brief and fleeting that it was barely there.

He didn't take it kindly. His mouth tightened as he drew his hand away. "You've been living in the big city too long if you call that a fair shake."

She could only think how *unfair* it was that the slightest contact with him was making her palm tingle. Flint's touch had always put fire in her blood.

"We're hardly long-lost friends," she reminded him, noting that he looked not only offended but also disappointed by her cool greeting. She couldn't be quite sure of his expression, though, for his face had always been unpredictably changeable.

"Once upon a time we were friendlier than this," he countered gruffly.

"Once upon a very short time, Flint."

"Yep." He rubbed the back of his neck. "Short. You can say that again. Makes me wonder why I drove all the way over here to get you."

Brynn stared at him. "What do you mean?"

"Arch and Maggie couldn't come at the last minute."

"Why not?" She had a sudden fear that her father's health had gotten worse. "What's wrong?"

"A half dozen of their sheep fell sick overnight with a virus. I owed your folks a favor, anyway, so I'm paying it back by coming to fetch you."

"It must be a big favor you owe them," she said, "or you wouldn't have come."

"Maybe I would've come if you'd asked me to, Brynn, but you never asked. Not for the past five years since you gave me hell and walked out on me."

Faced with Flint, Brynn had an instant's flashback of the day she married him. No. She wouldn't think of the wedding. She'd only remember why the marriage had been doomed from the start—because of Flint's love for her identical twin sister, Laurel.

"Looks like I'm wasting my valuable time here," Flint muttered. He shoved his hands into the pockets of his Levi's jacket. "Big mistake."

Brynn said, "Didn't you stop to think that I could rent a car here and drive myself home?"

"Hell, woman, that was my number one first thought."

"Why didn't you keep it in mind, then?"

"Just for your information, Brynn, snow's falling faster than the plows can clear it off the highway up on Mount Hood. You starting to see my point?"

"Not in the least. I know how to use tire chains and drive in snow, just as well as you do."

He scowled. "The point is, I came in my Bronco and wouldn't go back over Hood in anything less than a four-wheel drive with studded tires. You wouldn't be smart to try it in a car."

"I'd be smart to drive the car the long way around on Route 22," she said, "which is exactly what I'll do."

Flint shook his head. "No you won't, since 22 is closed. And Route 126 is snowed shut, too. I checked all the highway advisories before I left."

"I'll rent a four-wheel drive then, and go over Hood," Brynn said, sounding far more decisive to herself than she felt. Flint was completely flustering her.

She had known she was still in love with him, but she hadn't known how much until right now. She wasn't going to show even the slightest hint of it, though. She was determined he'd see only the bitterness she felt toward him. Not the love, not ever again. Loving him had shattered her emotions. Leaving him had caused her more pain than he'd ever know.

"Besides being a waste of money, renting a four-wheel drive doesn't make sense," Flint argued.

Brynn didn't intend to back down. "Having you take me home doesn't make sense, either, favor or no favor."

"Now look here, Brynn. I promised your folks I'd get you home safe. Besides, like they said, maybe it's time the two of us quit holding a few of our grudges against each other."

"Our differences aren't their business."

"You're still the one holding the biggest grudge, Brynn."

She lifted her chin. "I'm the one with the biggest reason."

"After five years, I've started edging past my complaints," he advised gruffly. "You still haven't started on yours, I guess."

"Good guess," she affirmed. "And I can't see any reason to start, either."

"Well, whatever you think, I'm taking you home to Arch and Maggie."

"No, thank you. I brought my two cats and you hate cats, so you're not taking us anywhere." She walked past him toward the baggage claim.

Flint followed and caught up with her. "The problem isn't me hating cats. It's you hating *me*. That's what you're really saying, isn't it?"

"I'm saying you can pay back your favor to Mom and Dad some other time, Flint. I'll drive myself—and my cats—home today."

She moved ahead of him again and stepped onto the escalator leading down to ground level and a reunion with Mickey and Minnie. "Dammit, Brynn. I didn't drive all the way here to go back without you. Your folks aren't the only reason I came, either."

Brynn said, "I know your other reason—you need a fill-in cook at the ranch and I'd be awfully convenient while I'm in the vicinity, wouldn't I?"

"So happens I've hired somebody."

"Congratulations. At least there's one thing we don't have to argue about."

"Look, the cook I hired can't start for two weeks. He's got to give notice at the job he's leaving. So you're right about me needing a fill-in cook."

"Namely me," Brynn said, "if I'm interested in filling in and saving the day for you."

"Well, now that you mention it . . . you wouldn't be interested, would you?"

She shook her head. "I'm not spending my vacation at Wilder Butte Ranch."

"Good thing you aren't, too," he rejoined curtly. "I don't need a cook badly enough to put out my welcome mat for a city-slick chef. You probably can't remember how to dish up rib-stickin' chow like you used to."

Brynn stiffened her spine. "I remember plenty about feeding you and your hired hands. All you married me for was to..." Her throat tightened against speaking the whole, tormenting truth.

"To what?"

"To bake biscuits and chili, and to . . ."

"Dammit, Brynn. Whatever's still stuck in your craw, spit it out. What else?"

The words bubbled up from a world of hurt. "To be your body double for Laurel! That's what!"

Flint's abrupt, stony silence behind her told her she had spit out more than he expected. She hadn't meant to cruelly blurt out the main reason for their marriage—and their subsequent divorce—just like that, where everyone on the escalator could hear. Flint had prodded it out of her, and now they were both embarrassed. If she could take the hurtful words back, she would.

Nonetheless, she had spoken the truth. Five years ago she had left him for that reason.

Brynn went straight to the first car rental counter, and told the clerk, "I need a four-wheel drive."

Behind her, Flint rumbled, "The hell you do."

"Sorry," the clerk said, "they're all taken, the weather being so bad in the mountains and ski areas."

"Seeing my point yet, Brynn?" Flint mocked.

She gave him a withering look over her shoulder, then went to the next rental counter. No luck there, either. All the way down auto row, from Avis to the Rent-A-Wreck hotline, there wasn't an all-weather vehicle to be had.

She turned away from the hotline phone and saw Flint rolling an empty luggage cart toward the baggage carousel. His long stride was eating up floor space and, as she watched him, she wished she could ignore the way his Levi's hugged his lean hips and muscled thighs. She saw women's eyes following him, and knew those women were thinking, *What a hunk!*

Brynn couldn't help thinking the same thing. Flint had a bigger-than-life charisma that wouldn't quit. He also had the personality—bold and self-assured, almost to the point of cocky—that backed it up.

"C'mon Brynn," Flint urged over his shoulder. "Here comes your gear."

Brynn switched her attention from Flint's cowboy charisma to the two cat carriers coming into view on the baggage carousel. Hearing Mick and Minn's distressing meows, she felt a perverse pleasure in knowing that Flint—a dog lover—would have to grit his teeth and put up with the feline duet all the way home. He wouldn't endure it kindly, either, from all that she knew of him. "I'm coming," she called back to him, wishing that nothing more than pet preferences had stood between her and Flint five years ago.

Unfortunately, their insoluble problem had been unrequited love. Brynn had never had Flint's true love; he had never had Laurel's.

Comforting him after Laurel threw him over—and trying to fill Laurel's place in his heart—had been the

second of Brynn's two great mistakes. Her first had
been to fall for her own sister's beau.

Back then, Brynn had thought there could be no
greater emotional pain than secretly loving a man who
was taken. Since then she had learned that nothing hurt
as much as being wife to a man whose heart would always belong to her twin sister. Talking in his sleep, he'd
often spoken Laurel's name. Never Brynn's.

Brynn had finally faced reality, abandoned hope and
forced herself out of the marriage. If only she had been
able to force Flint out of first place in her heart . . .

Now, how was she going to get through a long drive
home with the ex-husband she still loved?

2

FLINT DROVE his red Bronco out of Portland onto Highway 26. He wished the vehicle had a soundproof trunk
for the cats, or that Brynn would make an effort to shut
them up. He thought she should at least apologize for
their incessant complaints, but she hadn't said one
word since leaving the airport with him.

He flexed his fingers around the steering wheel,
knowing that Brynn had little use for him, knowing he
pretty much deserved it. But he knew he didn't deserve
those damn cats yowling their fool heads off back there.

"Are they hungry or what?" he grumbled.

"No, they're just understandably upset by their first
trip away from home."

"You should have boarded them in a kennel."

She gave him a narrow sideways look, then turned
her head to the back and put her finger to her lips.
"Shh." Miraculously the caterwauling stopped.

Flint blinked. "That's all it takes? Just you telling
them to shush?"

"That's all," Brynn replied, nodding. "They're very
well trained."

"You mean you could have shut them up all this time,
yet you didn't?"

"If you were bothered, you should have said something."

"You know they were driving me nuts."

She didn't acknowledge his retort, or say anything else. Her cool silence was a reproach and now the air was thick with it, reminding him of why he was worse than a cow-flop in his ex-wife's eyes. He hadn't expected to be greeted with hugs and kisses, but he'd hoped that time would have softened the hardest feelings that Brynn held against him.

Five years seemed to have hardened her heart instead, he thought impatiently. She was acting brittle, ready to splinter apart. And God in heaven, she still looked just like her twin sister.

He hadn't known how he'd react to seeing Brynn after so long. He'd been surprised that he hadn't thought *Laurel!* the first moment at the airport. That old feeling he'd feared so much, that love spasm, hadn't been there after all. There was no arguing that Brynn and Laurel would always be the mirror image of each other, but the visual impact was gone now.

He wondered if it meant he was finally breaking free of the past. A look over at Brynn told him he'd never be free until Brynn forgave him—and maybe herself, too.

"We've got a three-hour drive ahead," he said. "Making small talk would pass the time, but if you'd rather cuss me to hell and back instead, go ahead and give me a piece of your mind."

"What would that accomplish?" she murmured, turning her face away from him.

"It might clear the air in here." He adjusted the heat lever on the dashboard. "Warm enough for you?"

"Yes." She kept her eyes on the passing scenery.

"Quit giving me the silent treatment, Brynn. There's got to be something neutral we can talk about." He paused, willing her to respond. "How's Armand since I last saw him?"

"Fine."

"And?" he prodded relentlessly.

She seemed to realize he wasn't going to give up any time soon. "Armand is the same as ever. A jolly, bald elf who rules the kitchen with an iron hand."

Flint smiled. He had always liked Armand. "I wish he could rule my own kitchen from now on. If I can't find a temporary cook until the new one can start the job, I'll be up a creek without a canoe."

"I'm not for hire, Flint, if that's what you're still hoping."

"Hope is all I've got," he admitted. "That and a house full of guests needing three meals a day."

"What happened to the cook you had?"

He shrugged. "She didn't like being way out fifty miles from Bend. Didn't like cooking dude ranch food, or dishing up chow to my rowdy cowhands, either. You name it, she had something against it."

"Including you?"

"Including me," he lied. The truth was that the cute young cook had taken a lusty fancy to him. He hadn't been receptive to her advances, so she'd left in a huff without even giving notice.

Brynn asked, "Who's been cooking since she left?"

"Your mom."

"Mom?" Brynn murmured, looking surprised. "She never mentioned it."

"Look, Brynn, I can't offer you big-city wages, but I can give you fair pay. And room and board, too, for your convenience. Maggie says you'd rather work than have a vacation."

"I told her I'd work with her and Dad, thanks."

Flint puffed out a breath of air, losing patience. "Dammit. I'm not wanting you to double for Laurel, if that's all you're thinking."

She tightened her lips to keep them from trembling. "You can't look at me without seeing Laurel instead. You never could." Too late, she realized her words held a vindictive edge she hadn't intended and didn't even really feel.

"You don't have to hold it against me till the day you die," he said grimly.

"I wouldn't if it weren't true, Flint."

"It *was* true, and I'm deep-down sorry for that. You and I shouldn't have gotten married, that's for sure. In the first place, we were too damned young five years ago."

Brynn reflected that she had been nineteen when she married him, and he'd been twenty-four. "Age wasn't the problem, Flint."

"Immaturity was part of it," he argued, "for both of us. In the second place, you knew how things stood for me back then. I was on the rebound and you made yourself a little too available—"

"I don't want to talk about it," she insisted with a catch in her voice. "I wish you hadn't come to get me today."

"I'm starting to wish the same thing, Brynn."

Brynn shut her eyes, controlling the urge to break down and cry. Flint had never known how to handle tears. He had always stomped out to his saddle workshop and stayed there tooling leather until she'd regained a grip on her emotions.

Brynn took in a deep, calming breath and then put an extra effort into making small talk.

"Mom says you're busier than ever making saddles for rodeo superstars."

"Yep, I'm still at it, in between ranching cattle and registering guests. She told me you got promoted to some sort of assistant chef position."

"I'm one of many at the St. Martin. It's a big hotel with lots of chefs of every kind—sushi masters, *pâtissiers, boulangers*, and so on."

Flint was silent for a few minutes, then said, "I can't picture you living the city life. Or loving it, either, for that matter."

"I like it well enough, even though I suspect I'll always be a country girl at heart." She glanced back at the cats. "City life is all they've ever known. What they can see of it, that is, from my apartment windows."

"Do they have names?"

"Of course. Mickey and Minnie."

"As in Mouse?" Flint asked with an expression of droll disbelief.

She nodded, unable to suppress a smile at the face he made. "That's who they reminded me of when they were kittens. Didn't Mom tell you I've got cats?"

"Nope, even though she talks about you—and Laurel—a lot."

Brynn looked away, out the window at the town they were passing through—Sandy, Oregon. A part of her wanted to remark that Laurel was happy in Boise, but that would only hurt Flint and remind him of Laurel jilting him.

Despite some rocky times, Brynn and Laurel had always maintained a certain closeness, through thick and thin, from childhood on. She and her twin kept in regular touch, despite the distance they lived from each other. Brynn wondered how he received Maggie's newsy chats about Laurel's two children and her rodeo-promoter husband.

Brynn stopped just short of thinking *poor Flint*. It wouldn't help her to feel sympathetic or want to comfort Flint. Sympathy would only bring it all back. Consoling him had led her to marry him in the first place, the worst mistake of her life.

"So," Flint said, "I hear you tied the knot again a couple of years ago."

She shifted uncomfortably in the seat. "No doubt you heard that I untied it again, too."

She had met her second husband, Kelly Reilley, at the culinary academy. He'd been—and still was—the essence of teddy-bear charm. Brynn had let him cheer and cajole her into marrying him.

Soon afterward, they'd both discovered they were cut out to be good buddies rather than spouses. Three months after getting married at city hall, they went back and got an amicable no-fault divorce.

Flint asked, "What's your last name now, by the way?"

"I've changed it back to McBride. It's surprising you didn't hear that along with everything else."

"Maybe I did and it slipped my mind. Your dad says it was a friendly split between you and Reilley, no hard feelings."

Not like what ripped us apart, Brynn thought, *but a divorce just the same. Even the friendliest split has a failure at the core, whether it's faulty judgment, lack of commitment, irreconcilable differences, whatever.*

She said, "Mom and Dad aren't proud that I'm a two-time loser, but they keep their disappointment to themselves."

"They just want you and Laurel to be happy. That's all."

"She is," Brynn said.

"You don't act like you are," he observed frankly.

"You don't either, Flint."

He nodded, looking solemn. "You're right about that. Rustling up a cook for the next week or so would give me one reason to smile, though."

"Maybe losing your cook is a sign that you should quit taking in paying guests at Wilder Butte."

"Or a sign that you should fill in between the cook I lost and the one I've hired," he argued.

"So that you could pretend I'm Laurel again, even though you say you wouldn't?" Brynn blurted out, crossing her arms over her chest. "No. I've been there before and I'm not going back."

"I never meant to hurt you, Brynn. It wasn't anything I could help at the time."

"Or help right now, either," she muttered, tightening her arms.

Flint's jaw clenched. "How am I substituting you for Laurel right now? All I'm asking you to do is substitute-cook for a couple of weeks."

"Just leave me alone about cooking, because I'm not available. I know what your underlying reason is. Okay?"

"Okay, I admit I've got one."

Brynn nodded knowingly, but his next words surprised her.

"It's one way I can see for us to get civil with each other, Brynn. That's what I really want out of it. Having an ex-wife who hates me isn't my idea of living right—it chews on me, every day."

"You're not the only one to wish it never happened, Flint." Brynn felt tears stinging behind her eyelids again, dismaying proof that she was wrong to think she'd never cry again over Flint Wilder.

He said, "You still think it was mostly my fault?"

Brynn wasn't sure which way to answer. For five years she had blamed Flint more than herself for the mistake they'd made. Now, though, she wasn't so sure. The surprise of seeing Flint and being with him was shaking her up, making her beliefs about the past seem less clear-cut than they'd been for so long.

"I do my best not to think about it," she finally answered.

Flint didn't continue the conversation, and Brynn slowly started unwinding in the warmth of the heater as the miles rolled by. The rhythmic *whis-a-whisk* sound of the window wipers lulled the tension out of her neck and shoulders.

She watched icy rain barrage the windshield for a while, then dropped her head back against the headrest, closed her eyes and let her mind drift.

THE NEXT THING BRYNN KNEW, Flint was shaking her shoulder, saying, "Brynn, wake up."

She opened her eyes and found herself looking up into his penetrating blue gaze. His face was just a few inches away from hers. So close that she could inhale his outdoorsy scent, feel his warm breath on her cheek.

"What?"

"The highway's closed."

She glanced around, straightened in her seat and realized that the Bronco was halted in a line of cars and snowplows at a roadblock. Up ahead she saw the red and yellow flashing lights of patrol and road-service vehicles. It was snowing now, huge flakes that made the mountain world outside downy white.

"How did we reach the snow line so fast?"

"Fast, hell. It's been slow going the past hour while you catnapped."

She blinked. "Hour?"

"You were out." He gestured at the cats behind her. "Them, too. Stay put here while I go see how long we're going to be held up here."

He grabbed a rawhide overcoat and a battered Stetson out of the back seat and got out of the Bronco. Frigid air rushed in, fogging the windows. Brynn had to wipe a spot clear on the windshield to see out.

"Meow?" Mickey inquired.

"We're not there yet," Brynn informed him. "Shh."

Mick subsided into silence and Brynn kept her eyes fixed on Flint. When she'd first awakened, she had thought he was going to kiss her. For an instant, she had wanted a kiss from him more than anything in the world. She had almost laced her fingers behind his neck and pulled his head down to hers.

What a relief that she hadn't actually done it! If she had, he would most likely have pretended she was Laurel and responded to the illusion.

Well, there was no way to stop looking like Laurel, Brynn thought. Not short of dying her own hair a different color, or growing it out long, or wearing colored contact lenses to change her appearance.

"Forget that," Brynn murmured to herself, aware that her gray eyes and short, naturally curly blond hair were her and her twin's best features.

Physically, she and Laurel were exact duplicates. Their personalities weren't carbon copies, though, which Brynn attributed to Laurel's being born first. Laurel had always plunged headfirst through life, while Brynn lagged several steps behind. Laurel, so gregarious and outgoing, the crowd pleaser; Brynn, more cautious and careful, lost in the crowd around Laurel.

Brynn thought back to the day at the Crooked River Roundup when she and Laurel both fell in love with Flint at first sight. Laurel had been the rodeo queen, picked to present the silver trophies and blue ribbons to the winners, and Flint had won big that day. He'd ended up the all-around champion, as well as cowboy of the year.

He'd fallen for Laurel, at first sight, like a bull-dogged steer. Laurel had taken him, the top rodeo superstar in the nation, right in stride. Brynn had sat in the crowd and watched from a distance.

Watching Flint from a similar distance now, she saw him talking with a state patrolman. The officer was grinning, shaking Flint's hand, looking overjoyed. *A rodeo fan*, Brynn thought. She saw Flint leave him and head back to the Bronco.

He swept off his snow-crowned hat and got in. "Avalanche up ahead, big one that won't be cleared until sometime tomorrow."

Brynn grimaced. "That long?"

He tossed his hat into the back. "I've got a ski cabin back a mile the way we came. We can stay there until tomorrow morning."

Brynn pictured herself alone with Flint all night. No. "We passed several motels in Sandy," she recalled. "Let's backtrack and stay there."

"How many motels will take two cats? We know my cabin will." His tone took on a gruff note. "As long as they both keep their yaps shut, that is. Besides, it's getting dark and snowing harder."

"Is there a telephone to let Mom and Dad know we've been held up?"

"No, but the neighbors next door to my cabin have one. They live there year-round. Except for a phone, my place is stocked up with everything else we'll need. Food, dry firewood, hot water."

"I don't know, Flint," Brynn hedged. "Sandy is farther to drive, but . . ."

"The cabin is our best bet, with two cats, Brynn."

Brynn started to think he was right, considering that the hotel she worked in didn't allow pets. Motels probably had similar rules. The cabin presented no problem in that sense, and Mick and Minn had been confined in their carriers too long. Poor things.

Flint kept on arguing his case. "I hate motels. I stayed in one too many on the rodeo circuit." He put the gearshift into reverse. "The neighbor keeps the access lane plowed with his snow tractor."

"If it's not plowed when we get there, we go back to Sandy," Brynn said firmly, reattaching her seat belt.

"We'll see first," Flint replied.

He turned the Bronco around. Brynn squinted through the windshield, unable to see more than a few yards into the storm. Gusts of wind rocked the truck and swirled huge snowflakes into the headlamp beams, giving her a sense of vertigo.

After doubling back slowly for a mile, Flint turned off the highway onto a narrow lane. Brynn peered through the windshield, relieved to see that the lane was

better plowed than the highway. It was also more pro-
tected from storm winds and snowfall, lined on both
sides by a dense growth of evergreens that formed an
overhead canopy.

"Shelter from the storm," she murmured, seeing the
glow of house lights farther ahead.

"That's the neighbors' place. They're a retired couple. Come to think of it, they've got a cat, so maybe we
can borrow some food and litter from them."

Brynn was surprised at him sparing a thought for
Mick and Minn's welfare. He stopped in front of the
house, got out and went inside. He came back a few
minutes later with a plastic box, a bag of litter and a
container of Kitty Kibbles.

"I phoned your folks. We're all set. Just a short hike
across the way to a warm fire and a hot meal." He
wheeled the Bronco in a U-turn and parked across the
lane. Brynn could make out the dim, angular shape of
an A-frame cabin. The snow was knee-deep on the un-
cleared path to the door. Wearing twill slacks and suede
flats, she wasn't dressed for wading through it.

"I'll need the boots I brought in my suitcase," she told
Flint.

"Which one?"

"I don't remember. They're both locked." She found
her purse and started rummaging in it for the luggage
keys.

Flint got out of the Bronco. "I can carry you inside,"
he said through his open door.

"No. I have boots."

He strode around to her door and opened it. "Undo your seat belt."

"I will, as soon as I find my—"

She broke off as he loomed over her, released the belt himself and scooped her out in his arms.

"First time I've enjoyed myself today," he said.

The purse in Brynn's grasp kept her from beating her fists against Flint's chest, but she didn't hold back from kicking her feet and protesting his he-man behavior.

"Flint, put me d—"

"I know you want nothing to do with me," Flint rumbled. "You don't have to keep repeating it."

He cradled Brynn's body in an uncompromising, effortless hold, but she didn't let it stop her vigorous protests.

"Put me down, Flint Wilder!"

"No, ma'am, I'm taking you all the way in," he said, striding through the snow.

"This is ridiculous. I have two legs and—"

"Yes, ma'am, you sure have. Mighty nice legs, if memory serves me right."

"And two feet, and—"

"Yep," he interrupted again, "size seven narrow, the last time I looked."

"And I also have boots of my own," she insisted through gritted teeth.

Flint was obstinate. "I remember you hated having cold feet. You even wore socks to bed. Sexiest socks I ever did see, too."

"You're being overly macho, Flint."

"Chivalrous," he corrected, reaching the door and kicking away the snow banked against it.

"Put me down. Now!"

He didn't relent right away, and then when he did, it seemed to Brynn that it took a long time. Brynn was breathless, aware of every muscled inch of his body against hers by the time he allowed her toes to touch down. She had to cling to him for balance, although she wanted to resist needing him for anything.

The snowy wind whipped all around, blowing Flint's hat off his head. He didn't move to retrieve it, seemed unconcerned that it was tumbling away over the snow.

"Your hat," Brynn said.

"It won't go far," he replied, angling his face down toward hers. His tone lowered to a husky murmur. "Hell of a night to be out in the cold."

For the second time, Brynn had the heart-stopping feeling that her ex-husband was going to kiss her. Once again, she felt a keen desire for him to do it. He was certainly holding her close enough, both arms around her.

"It's good to see you, Brynn. I know you're not pleased to see me, but I can't help that. Can't help this right now, either..."

He dipped his head, touched his lips to hers, and Brynn's breath stopped. For one wild, unbridled moment she didn't care if Flint was pretending to embrace and kiss Laurel. His lips were warm, tempting, seeking a response. Brynn gave up and responded and he tightened his hold on her. She told herself she'd stop him— *now*—but that wasn't quite possible. He was more than she could resist, for more reasons than she could name. He was bringing back memories of love. And marriage. And passionate sex.

Her common sense broke through, warning, *This is your ex-husband you're kissing!*

She found the strength to stop the kiss, but not enough willpower to break out of Flint's arms. "Wh-what did you do that for?"

"I'm not sure." He tilted his snowcapped head as if his own actions puzzled him. "Why did you let me?"

"I wasn't given much choice, Flint." She backed out of his relaxed hold so he could unlock the door. Then he stepped inside and flipped a switch. Lights went on indoors and outside.

The cabin was one big room with no loft. Heavy timber beams led the pine ceiling up to a steep peak. A river-stone fireplace took up one side wall, a galley kitchen lined the rear wall, a long sofa and comfy armchairs half circled the fireplace. She walked through and found a small bathroom tucked behind the kitchen.

Flint gestured at the sofa. "It makes into a king bed."

"*One* bed?"

3

"WE CAN MANAGE WITH ONE bed," Flint said. "It's only for one night."

"This won't do." Brynn shook her head firmly at him.

"It'll have to pull double duty until morning comes."

"No. We're not doubling up between the same sheets."

A teasing glint came into Flint's eyes. "You never had any objection to sharing one bed with me while we were married."

"I object now, Flint, for reasons I'm sure you remember as well as I do."

"I remember, all right. Yes, ma'am. Who could forget the sensational sex we used to have in bed together?" His lips quirked in a baiting grin. "That's your whole problem with doubling up tonight."

Brynn retorted, "It should be a problem for you, as well. And I resent your teasing tone."

He ignored her resentment, taunting, "Who don't you trust, me or yourself?"

"I've had it up to here with your snickering, Flint." She settled her hands on her hips, exasperated by him, determined to stand her own ground. "Answer your questions yourself."

"The answer is you don't trust either of us," he said with a sharpening edge in his tone, "because we used to sizzle in bed together no matter what else was wrong between us."

"That fact alone is all the reason we both need to sleep apart tonight," she insisted.

His tone began to cut instead of tease. "Just once today I'd like to hear from you that being married to me had one great thing going for it from the get-go to the bitter end."

"Just once," Brynn rejoined tartly, "I'd like you to acknowledge my objections to this bed!"

"You're objecting to me, not the bed!"

"After getting kissed against my will on your doorstep, you expect me to feel safe sleeping with you? Ha!"

"I'll spend the night in a chair, then," he said, a scowl darkening his face. He went back out the door and slammed it shut.

Brynn slumped against the wall and surveyed the cabin with utter dismay. It was compact and cozy, perfect for one person or a couple with no children. It was shelter from the storm, but completely inappropriate for a divorced couple. Close quarters. One bed. A long night ahead.

She shivered. The air around her was only a fraction warmer than outside. Seeing baseboard heat units and a wall thermostat, she turned up the temperature from low to high, then found matches on the mantel and lit the logs and kindling that were arranged on the grate.

Flint stomped back in, a snowman with a cat carrier in each hand. "Don't let them loose until I'm through going in and out," he warned, giving the door another slam on his way out.

"He thinks you'd run out in a snowstorm," Brynn scoffed to Mickey and Minnie. "That's how much he doesn't know about cats."

She went to investigate the kitchen. The cupboards were full of canned food and dry goods; there was a well-stocked liquor cabinet; the small refrigerator held some beer and several bottles of white wine. She took out a container of buttered-rum mix and entertained the idea of aiming it at Flint's thick head.

He came in with her suitcases and set them down against one wall. "Look," he said curtly, "can we agree to stop wrangling for the next hour or so? Long enough to warm up from the cold and have some dinner in relative peace?"

"I suppose so," she conceded, "if we both put our minds to it."

He gave a harsh but relieved sigh. "You see anything you'd like to have for dinner?"

"Beef stew," she replied. "I'll heat it up for us."

"Good, I'm starved."

Brynn felt the same, since she'd only nibbled on the tasteless in-flight snack the airline had served. She made another concession to peace by offering, "I'll spice up the stew somehow, and make dumplings from biscuit mix."

"Double the recipe," Flint urged. "I didn't have much of a lunch."

"Would you care for a hot buttered rum first?" Brynn held up the mix she'd found.

"Thanks." He nodded, heading to the door again. "I'll get the cat box and track down my hat."

Brynn hoped he wouldn't find his Stetson. Losing it would serve him right for kissing her on the doorstep. She wasn't going to let him get that close again.

Putting a curb on her tempestuous emotions, she set a kettle on to boil. When Flint returned with the box, she put it in the bathroom, took the cats in there and set them free.

The fire was roaring on the hearth and Flint was pouring rum into two mugs when she came out of the bathroom. She noticed that Flint's Stetson was on his head, and that snow was melting on the shoulders of his rawhide coat.

"You got your hat back from the wind, I see."

He nodded. "I figured I might have to eat it for dinner in case you locked me out of here."

"The thought crossed my mind," Brynn assured him, going to stand by the fire.

"There's no doubt I'd rather be eating your home-made dumplings."

She turned her back on his steady blue gaze, warning herself not to be affected by his gruff conciliatory compliment. After all, he was a man who desperately needed a chef for the next couple of weeks. That was the only reason he was making peace offerings and throwing praise around like confetti.

"When did you buy this place?" she asked, to change the topic.

"Last summer. I spent a few days around here trout fishing and met the neighbors at a stream up the hill.

They had this cabin for sale and I bought it on impulse. What do you think?"

She nodded in approval. "It's a nice getaway."

"You've got the honor of being my first guest here."

"Your first emergency guest, at least," she murmured, turning to warm her back and look at him again.

"The first guest, period," he insisted. "Número uno."

Brynn remained dubious, having heard from her mother that Flint dated occasionally. It seemed likely that he'd had female company here, despite his claim to the contrary. He was simply being a gentleman about it, she told herself.

Brynn watched him spoon the butter-spice mix into the mugs and stir in hot water from the kettle. His hands, strong and square, brought back erotic memories of him caressing her body, arousing her deepest passions.

Brynn pivoted and faced the fire again, tried to think of something besides Flint's masterful lovemaking, tried to hold prosaic thoughts. Of heating stew. Of cooking dumplings.

Of making love in the king-size bed.

Flint spoke right behind her. "Here's your drink."

"Thanks, bartender." She turned halfway and took it from him, careful not to let her fingers touch his.

"Cheers, Brynn."

She took a sip. "Same to you."

"Nice bonfire you got started," he said, leaning against the stone mantel.

"You get the credit for setting the logs," she replied, reluctant to accept any compliments from him. "I only had to open the damper and light a match."

Flint put his mug on the mantel and took off his coat and hat. He stamped his boots on the hearth rug to knock off melting snow, then took up his drink again.

"Good thing the avalanche came down past where the lane turns off. All in all, I'd say we lucked out, wouldn't you?"

She shrugged. "Except for the bed."

Flint raised an eyebrow, appraising Brynn's expression. She looked edgy, wary, as if she already suspected that he didn't plan to sleep in a chair tonight. Damn right, he didn't. With a long drive through winter weather ahead of him tomorrow, he'd need a decent night's rest. A chair wouldn't give any rest to a six-footer like him.

He felt something touch his lower leg and found the two cats sniffing him. *Let them sleep in the chairs.* Brynn moved to the kitchen, calling their names, and they followed her, meowing, with their tails up. Flint warmed himself at the fireplace and watched her put food and water in bowls for them.

He surprised himself again by not thinking of Laurel as he looked at Brynn. Brynn hadn't changed visibly, so that wasn't making the difference. It was something else, something he couldn't pin down. Seeing her now, and knowing how he'd used her, caused him as much pain as he'd once felt over getting jilted by her sister.

Still, marrying Brynn hadn't been all his doing. Brynn had known how torn up he'd been after Laurel.

She could have stayed away from Wilder Butte and let him steep his misery in a bottle of tequila night after night. She could have kept her own love for him a secret instead of surprising him with it.

But no, she had come over and poured the Cuervo down the drain, sobered him up, cooked him dinner, kept him company. And simply loved him. She'd made it possible, and then easy, for him to pretend he hadn't lost his fiancée to another man.

Flint wasn't pretending now, or at least he didn't think he was. Although he didn't quite understand why he'd kissed Brynn on the doorstep, he was sure it wasn't because of any residual longing for Laurel.

He also knew that his needs weren't the same now as they'd been before Brynn left him, when he had been too selfish and self-centered to reject the physical and emotional solace she had offered him.

Thinking back on the restless, rowdy life he'd led in his rodeo days, he could see how shallow, shaky and egocentric his ethics and values had once been. Not now. Retiring from the arena and becoming a rancher had gradually brought his ego down to earth and set his priorities straighter than they'd ever been.

Older now, and tempered by past mistakes, he had a lot stronger hold on himself. So, then why was he thinking how hard it would be for him to stay on his own half of the bed tonight?

"Want some help with dinner?" he asked to distract his thoughts, even though he knew she'd always preferred being the only cook in the kitchen.

She shook her head and motioned him to stay out of her way, so he dropped into the biggest easy chair and stared into the flames on the hearth.

Savoring his drink, keeping an ear tuned to Brynn's movements, he heard her opening cans and setting a pan on the stove. She stirred something in a bowl. The sounds were active and busy, yet comforting. She was cooking dinner for him as she had done when they were married, and it eased his loneliness tonight as it had during their marriage. This day sure as hell hadn't gone the way it was supposed to, he mused. And it still had a ways to go.

"I don't remember whether you like rosemary or not," she said from the kitchen. "Do you?"

"Sure. Why?" He wondered what else she had forgotten about him.

"This stew needs it," she replied.

Flint said, "You're the expert." He took up a *Field & Stream* magazine and flipped it open, hoping it would draw his thoughts away from the sexual interest he was taking in his ex-wife.

Funny, he thought, that he hadn't started out this morning expecting his basic needs to go ballistic over Brynn. He'd thought he'd respond to reminders of Laurel, but not to Brynn alone.

He had no idea how to handle his unexpected urge to come on to Brynn. It wasn't as if he didn't know all about her, not as if he'd never kissed her or made love to her. He'd done both, as her husband, countless times. Yet, now he was feeling as if he'd somehow just met her and suddenly had to have her.

Lust was all there was to it, he assured himself. He was mature, with more than enough experience to recognize the source and nature of his primal responses.

He told himself not to want Brynn, not to feel the raw urge to have her. Or at least not pay it any close attention.

Which didn't do him a damned bit of good.

It was a relief to hear a knock on the door. "I'll get it," he told Brynn. "Must be the neighbor."

He turned on the outside light, opened the door and found a dainty little deer standing outside. A doe, she had a red calico bandanna and a tick collar fastened around her neck. She raised one hoof and knocked again, twice, on the doorsill.

Flint could hardly believe what he was seeing. "Brynn, come here. Look at this."

She came and looked. "What on earth?"

As they both stood there in disbelief, the animal stepped halfway into the cabin and shook itself off.

"Shoo," Brynn said, waving a tentative hand at it.

Undeterred, it stepped all the way inside, switched its tail and glanced around.

"It's not afraid," Flint marveled.

"Not one bit," Brynn agreed. "What does it...want?"

In silent answer to Brynn's question, the deer went to the fire and curled up in front of it on the hearth rug. Brynn and Flint stared openmouthed at it, and then looked at each other.

"That scarf didn't tie itself around this animal's neck," Flint reasoned. "I'd better check this out next door." He took up his coat and hat.

Brynn caught his arm. "What if this deer is sick? What if it has rabies and attacks my cats?"

"Stay out of its way while I'm gone. Close the cats in the bathroom. Yourself, too."

He went out the door, leaving it open for the deer to go out if it wished, and Brynn hustled the cats from the kitchen into the bathroom. She kept the door open a crack and peered at the deer.

It looked back at her with huge, brown eyes, seeming perfectly calm and at home on the hearth. Brynn felt rather ridiculous to be barricaded in the bathroom, but then the whole situation was beyond the pale.

Within a few minutes, Flint returned, chuckling. "We can relax," he said. "She's tame, harmless and house-broken. They adopted her from a petting zoo that went out of business. Do you mind if she visits here for a while?"

"No," Brynn decided, hovering in the bathroom doorway. "But I can't speak for Mick and Minn. They're strictly indoor cats who've never even seen a dog, much less a deer."

"Let them out and see what happens."

Holding her breath, Brynn released them. They ventured forth, eyed the strange animal and then tentatively approached it. After a few experimental sniffs of its scent, they switched their tails and returned to their food in the kitchen.

"Ignorance is bliss, I guess," Brynn murmured.

Flint returned his coat and hat to a peg on the wall and stamped the snow off his boots again.

"She's got a damned cute name," he said.

"Oh? What?"

"Matchmaker."

His tone was teasing and Brynn wasn't sure whether to believe him. "Sure," she scoffed as she poured out biscuit mix for dumplings. "I'll bet it's something more like Bambi."

"Honest to God, Brynn, it's Matchmaker. Cross my heart and kiss my shins."

"Well, she came to the wrong place," she mumbled.

He stroked the deer's ears, petted her head. "Maybe she'll match me up with the stand-in cook I need," he said. "If I'm lucky."

"My response to your offer is the same as before, Flint." But in the secret space of Brynn's heart a soft, silent voice was urging her to do it just for that short time.

She saw Matchmaker look over at her. The deer nodded its head, as if in agreement with the inner voice Brynn couldn't quite silence.

"No," Brynn murmured.

But neither Flint nor Matchmaker seemed to be getting the message. They both looked hopeful, Brynn thought. Especially Flint.

He went on making friends with Matchmaker while Brynn created a salad of canned artichoke hearts and black olives. She mixed up a pimento vinaigrette, then garnished the hearts with bottled capers. A package of granola and a tin of pie filling would bake into a nice fruit crisp for dessert.

"Who stocked the pantry for you?" she asked Flint.

He raised his eyebrows. "What tells you I didn't stock it myself?"

"This." She held up the jar of capers. "And all the other gourmet goodies . . . béarnaise sauce mix, balsamic vinegar, extravirgin olive oil."

He said, "You remember I don't know beans about fancy groceries, but you forgot I like rosemary spice."

Brynn set the jar aside. "Rosemary is an herb, not a spice. One more clue that you didn't round up the fancy groceries by yourself."

"A man can't hide a woman's touch, you mean."

A woman's touch? Meaning I'm not his first guest, after all, she concluded with an unsettling pang.

"It's a touch that's easy to see, Flint," she said, pretending to be neutral about it.

"I'll have to tell Amelia you noticed," he said. "It all came in a ritzy food basket she gave me for a cabin-warming present."

Brynn could just imagine Amelia giving him a bed-warming present, too. Every tart, tangy little caper on the salad tonight would remind him of Amelia's generosity, Brynn predicted, feeling wretched. She pictured Amelia as nothing less than drop-dead beautiful. And she was obviously a woman of good taste.

Aside from her taste in men.

Brynn quelled an urge to dump the salad into the sink. She curbed an even stronger impulse to hurl the stew pot at Flint for lying to her about not having any guests before this.

"Let's eat by the fire," Flint suggested. He sniffed the air. "Your cooking smells mighty fine, Brynn."

Brynn glanced up from assembling the cherry crisp. She pursed her lips tightly to convey how immune she was to any and all of his flattering comments. Fixing dinner tonight—and maybe breakfast tomorrow—was as far as she'd go toward being his stand-in cook. He'd better get used to the idea and figure out some other scheme to solve his problem.

"Mighty fine," he persisted as he rose from his chair and joined her in the kitchen.

Brynn muttered, "It's only canned stew."

He opened a cupboard that housed a wine rack. "Red or white with it?"

"Either one," she replied. "There aren't many rules left for which wine goes with what." Brynn couldn't imagine why Amelia hadn't already informed him of that.

He took out a bottle, uncorked it and poured the wine into two stemmed glasses. "You'd better give it a taste test," he said. "I don't drink enough red wine to tell good *Pinot* from bad *Noir*."

Brynn tasted it and pronounced, "An exceptional Pinot Noir." Even though the bottle had probably been the centerpiece of his cabin-warming gift.

"Just like that you know good from bad, huh?"

Nodding, she took another sip. "François is a great teacher," she couldn't help saying.

Flint was silent for a moment. "What does he teach?"

"All about wine. I owe everything I know about reds to his passion for them."

"Is that all he teaches you?"

She started to make a flippant reply but stopped, surprised to see a sudden spark of emotion in Flint's eyes. Jealousy? She caught her breath. An instant later, he looked down, leaving her uncertain of what she had seen.

"None of my business," he muttered. He brought his glass up and took a slow taste from it. "This *is* good."

Giving a cool glance at the bottle's expensive label, Brynn inquired, "From Amelia's gift basket?"

"From her husband, Hank," Flint replied. "They're the neighbors next door."

She blinked, then felt the most foolish smile begin to form on her lips. It quickly led to a chuckle. Fighting it, she turned away from Flint and placed the cherry crisp in the oven.

"What's so damned funny, Brynn?"

"François," she replied. "He's a friend of Armand's. The funny part is that he looks exactly like Santa Claus."

Flint laughed, sounding delighted to learn that François wasn't a hunk. "Really?"

"Beyond that," Brynn added, "he's a pompous twit about champagne. We have a running argument about California bubbly versus French bubbly. He refuses to do a blind tasting and settle the question."

"He must have done one of his own and found out he'd lose," Flint mused.

"I wouldn't doubt it."

Flint leaned against the counter, watching her work. "You've gotten downright sophisticated since you left Oregon."

"Meaning I was a country bumpkin before?"

"No, only you've got to admit you didn't know hay about wine back then."

"True," she conceded. "I didn't know hay about a lot of what I've learned since I moved to San Francisco."

"You're not anything like I was expecting, Brynn. You're so much more . . ."

Brynn almost held her breath. "More what?"

"Professional, I guess. Sophisticated isn't exactly the word."

"Maybe you meant to say I've grown up." Brynn turned away from him to ladle stew and dumplings into soup plates.

"Could be," he murmured. "Maybe both of us have."

With her back to Flint, she had the thrilling sensation that he couldn't keep his eyes off her, that he was thoroughly checking her out. She made herself remember why she shouldn't be uplifted by any attention he might be paying her. She couldn't let herself forget he was seeing Laurel, his long-lost love, not Brynn McBride.

It wasn't a sensation Brynn could control, though, especially not after the kiss he'd given her on the doorstep. Flint's nearness, his masculinity—well, it was flustering to say the least.

It brought back a memory of one summer evening in the kitchen at Wilder Butte ranch. . . .

Married to Flint only three weeks, she had been in the kitchen paring ripe, red apples for a pie when he came up behind her and spanned his hands around her waist. He slipped them up to her breasts, captivated her with seductive caresses, then lifted her onto the counter, facing him, and drew up the hem of her cambric skirt....

Brynn gave herself a sharp mental shake to stop the vivid memory from spinning out any further. She couldn't keep her cheeks from flaming with warmth as she faced Flint again and handed the plates of stew to him.

"You take these. I'll carry out the salad and wine."

"No, you won't," Flint said. "Sit down by the fire and relax."

His tone was decisive again, unbending, so Brynn went and sat on the couch. She found Mickey and Minnie catnapping on the hearth rug with Matchmaker, who was also asleep.

"I can hardly believe this scene," Brynn marveled to Flint.

He brought the food and utensils to the coffee table and settled down next to her. "Big little heart-warmer, isn't it?" He gave her a tongue-in-cheek look. "Two wild animals at peace with a tame one, I mean."

Brynn pretended to bristle in defense of her pets. "Mick and Minn aren't wild."

"To a mouse, they are." He raised his wineglass to her. "Cheers to the chef."

She surrendered a smile and accepted his toast. *"Bon appétit."*

"Heaven," Flint said after his first bite of salad. "I'm in heaven."

But Brynn was in hell about the feelings she still had for Flint. Her taut nerves diminished her appetite, even for her own cooking. She tasted the salad and found it more bland than heavenly; the herbed dumplings seemed equally unappealing.

Flint, however, ate as if the meal was the last one he'd ever get. He took several helpings and chided Brynn for picking at her food.

"No wonder you're thinner than you used to be," he said.

Now Brynn knew for sure that she hadn't imagined him eyeing her in the kitchen. The certainty brought another rush of heat to her cheeks, and a reminder of the erotic memory she had cut short earlier. This would be the longest night of her life!

4

AFTER DINNER, Brynn withdrew into the bathroom and took a shower while Flint did K.P. She mentally prepared herself to lock horns with him about the bed. No matter what, she wasn't going to make the mistake of slipping between the sheets with her ex-husband.

Brynn stepped out of the stall, dried off, and dressed in flannel pajamas. She buttoned the top right up to the collar, then put on fleecy socks and a woolen robe.

Set for a showdown, Brynn opened the bathroom door. She found Flint on the other side, poised to knock.

He lowered his hand. "You had me thinking you'd drowned."

She stepped into the hallway and replied, "Dressing to kill takes time."

"*Over*dressing," he corrected wryly, looking her up and down. "Are you ready for bed, or battle?"

"Both. You didn't sound sincere when you said you'd sleep in a chair."

"You're damn right I didn't," he replied firmly. "There's one sleeping arrangement here, ma'am. Take it or leave it."

"Flint, I'm not going to—"

He cut her short by entering the bathroom and slamming the door shut.

Resisting the urge to pound on the door and have her say, Brynn entered the main room. She saw that he'd opened up the sofa. Rosy firelight flickered on the thick down comforter Flint had spread over the bed. There were two pillows, leaving no doubt of where he intended to sleep. Perhaps in response to her earlier objections, he'd placed the pillows as far apart as possible.

Brynn would have liked to see a barbed wire fence strung down the center of the mattress. A ridiculous thought, which shouldn't even occur to an adult, twice-divorced woman. A thought that wouldn't have occurred to her at all if Flint had been Kelly Reilley tonight.

With Kelly, would she be wringing her hands about hopping into one bed with him? Not a chance. Sexual attraction hadn't been a defining element in her brief marriage to him. Sex had been nothing more than an occasional afterthought in their amiable relationship.

With Flint, however, sex had been superlative, satisfying and so frequent that . . . hmm. A platonic night in bed with Flint was as difficult to picture then as it was right now.

Behind her, she heard the bathroom door open.

"If you're thinking up a big argument," Flint growled, "think again. We're not going to draw straws for the bed. Nobody's spending the night in any damn chair, unless it's you by your own choice."

Brynn crossed her arms over the front of her robe and retorted, "Stay on your own side of the bed then. And remember that we're divorced."

"Give me a break," he muttered as he switched out the lights.

Brynn threw off her robe and slid under the covers. She pulled them up to her chin and watched Flint bank the fire. He was wearing an undershirt and boxers, more than he'd ever worn to bed as her husband.

Brynn squeezed her eyes shut, closing out the sight of his shoulder muscles stretching his knit shirt. Closing out any possibility of him seeing her eyes blaze with frustrated desire. Until today, she'd almost forgotten her libido, having stifled her own sexual needs far longer than she felt comfortable remembering.

The mattress dipped as Flint got into bed. Brynn kept perfectly still, listening to him punch his pillow a few times, one of his bedtime rituals she recalled from the six months she'd slept with him. He gave a gravelly, masculine sigh, then finally settled down.

"For what it's worth," he muttered, "good night."

Brynn made an appropriately indistinct reply and turned onto her side with her back to him. Quiet, if not peace, reigned at last. There was an occasional crackle from the fireplace, but no other sound.

Brynn mentally counted sheep from one to a hundred, and then hummed lullabies in her mind. After a while, she heard Flint's breathing slow down and segue into a deep, even tempo.

Unable to resist, she inched around onto her back again and sneaked a sidelong peek at him. The fire glow softened his handsome features and burnished his dark, tousled hair. He looked boyish, peaceful and vulnerable, so easy to love.

A wave of desolate longing swept through Brynn as she gazed upon his sleeping face. Tears blurred her vision and she turned away once more, feeling mournful and terribly alone on her own half of the bed.

"YES . . . OH, FLINT . . . kiss me . . . again. . . ."

Brynn's soft, murmuring sighs brought her half-awake and she had the sensation that she was in Flint's arms, lying face-to-face with him.

Flint had his lips pressed against the side of her throat, kissing her. He had one warm hand upon her pajama top, curved over her breast, and her own hands were behind him, stroking the hard muscles of his back through his T-shirt. He, too, was murmuring soft words of inducement and need. His husky breath steamed and sensitized her skin, her legs were loosely intertwined with his.

Not quite slumbering, nor awake, Brynn didn't make any great effort to wake up. In a willing, lingering haze, she let herself respond to what felt like lucid, wish-fulfilling dream, one she dreamed often about Flint, one she wanted never to end.

"Flint . . . yes . . ."

His shoulder muscles rippled under her fingertips as his mouth left her throat and captured her own mouth in a deep, delicious, ravishing kiss that brought his tongue thrusting against hers.

His fingers moved, molding the fabric of her pajama top over the taut peak of her breast. Her own fingers came forward from his back, traced over the front of his T-shirt and explored the hard contours of his chest.

Flint's breath caught, then rushed out. "Ah, so good, darlin'...so mmm..."

Eyes closed, she kept her mind afloat on a shallow sea of sleep. His musky male scent enveloped her, heightened her desire for him to continue kissing her and holding her tight against his aroused body.

Suddenly he went rigid. His possessive, caressing hand stopped in midmotion. She heard his breath pull in, felt him struggle to draw away.

"Brynn," he said in an urgent, ominous tone. "Hey, Brynn."

Her name, spoken twice and so clearly, forced her to open her eyes. "What?"

"Wake up." He slid his hand away from her breast.

Brynn jerked her own hands back from his chest. Her breath came in sharp, shocked gasps as she fully realized what she had more than half consciously let herself—and Flint—do.

Brynn edged to the other half of the mattress while Flint rolled over onto his back and rubbed his face. Then he swung his legs over the edge of the bed and sat up with his back to her.

"Jeez," he muttered, "how did that happen?"

Brynn crossed her arms over her throbbing breasts in the full, guilty knowledge that Flint's touch and his kisses had aroused her to a panting fever pitch.

"I told you one bed wouldn't do," she heard herself blurt out accusingly. "But, no, you had to insist."

He retorted, "Don't go putting all the blame on me again. You're at fault, too."

"For what?" Brynn was incensed, at her own behavior and at him.

"For knowing how to turn me on," Flint replied.

"You taught me how, Flint. Before you, I was—"

He took the words out of her mouth. "An innocent virgin. Here we go with the grudges again."

"I didn't start this day out wrong," she insisted. "You did, by picking me up at the airport."

"Fight, fight, fight," he growled, throwing off the comforter and getting out of bed. "It's all we've done since you got off the plane."

He stalked into the bathroom and shut the door behind him with a resounding slam.

"Meow?" Mickey asked from one of the armchairs, where he and Minnie had been sleeping.

"You two stay out of this," Brynn warned through gritted teeth.

She was at a complete loss to deal with the frustrated desire she felt thrumming within her. Her body craved physical release in the worst way. She remembered everything Flint used to do to satisfy her—and everything she used to do to satisfy him. During her brief marriage to him, he had taught her so well and brought her such unforgettable sexual pleasure.

It hadn't been enough, however, she belatedly reminded herself. As well as his body, she had wanted his heart. But Laurel had been carved on it.

Brynn heard Flint come out of the bathroom and open up a closet. He stepped into view a minute later carrying a comforter like the one on the bed.

"I flipped a coin," he said. "You get the bed to yourself. I get the armchairs pushed together." He eyed Mick and Minn in one of the chairs. "Could you make them move?"

Brynn coaxed them to come and sleep on the bed. Flint rolled his eyes impatiently during the protracted time it took the two cats to yawn, rise to all fours and stretch to and fro before they finally made the leap from chair to bed.

"Give me a good cow dog any day," he grumbled, pushing the chairs together to face each other with a leather ottoman in between.

Brynn couldn't help but notice that Flint's body was powerfully aroused within his boxers. He looked potent—and incredibly uncomfortable. *Poor Flint,* she found herself thinking. *Poor me, too.* "Flint, I—"

"Toss me my pillow, would you, please?"

Brynn tossed it to him. "You were right," she hesitantly offered as he settled into his makeshift bed. "The blame is half mine."

"Doesn't matter now," he said, wrapping the comforter around himself. "Get some sleep."

"If I can, you mean," Brynn quipped uneasily.

Flint gave a frustrated but forgiving sigh. "Yeah. If we both can."

Settling down under her covers, Brynn stared up at the open-beam ceiling. The bed felt off kilter now without Flint on the other side. What a night. Cooling down wouldn't be simple or painless.

After a while, Flint said, "You were right about something, too, Brynn."

"What?"

"That bed being too small for the two of us. You insisted it would never do, and it didn't."

"Well, it's over and done with." Brynn hadn't thought he'd ever admit to being a little too cocky and confident.

"I guess I've been bunking alone too long," he added in a gruff, utterly revealing undertone.

Brynn was amazed by his admission. Why not meet him halfway and make her own confession?

She sighed. "You aren't the only one, Flint. I bunk alone, too."

"No wonder we both lost our heads, then."

She nodded. "It all adds up. Good night."

"Night, Brynn."

Sooner than she would have believed at that moment, Brynn fell asleep.

5

FLINT WOKE FIRST the next morning. He tiptoed around,
brewing coffee, blessing the clear skies that dawn had
brought. Brynn's cats sat up next to her sleeping form
and watched him over the back of the sofa. Flint en-
vied them the spot they'd had last night beside Brynn's
warm, womanly body. Sleeping alone was the loneli-
est damn thing; his own body still ached for release.

Up all night, he mused grimly, was more than just a
figure of speech. Wearing his shirttail untucked helped
hide his continued discomfort. The minute Brynn
opened her eyes, he'd hop in the shower and solve the
persistent problem. Running the noisy shower now
might disturb her sleep.

A muffled knock came at the door. He opened it and
found Matchmaker wanting to visit again.

"Shh," he cautioned her as he let her in.

She nuzzled his hand, then went to the fire and the
hearth rug, where she settled down in perfect ease and
comfort. The cats left Brynn and joined the deer. Flint
watched them sniff the doe and rub up against her.

He had to smile at their friendly antics, although he'd
never seen any sense in keeping cats for anything but
catching barn mice. He had three or four felines out in

his own hayloft. And that's where they stayed their whole lives through.

The pretty little deer, though, was a different story altogether. He'd love to have a pet like her at the ranch, charming the boots off the guests.

Flint poured himself a cup of coffee and set to wondering if his neighbors next door would ever agree to part with their adopted pet. Or maybe they knew of another doe like Matchmaker, one needing a home.

She was the damned sweetest little thing, polite as you please and not the least bit of trouble. There was, he thought, something sort of magical about that animal. He debated whether to run the adoption idea past Brynn after she woke up.

If she woke up, he corrected himself, tiptoeing over to see if she was still dead to dawn. She had always been a sound sleeper, at least during the time he'd been married to her. It appeared that she still was, and the dreamy interlude last night was all the more proof of it.

She had been so pliant and responsive in his arms . . . sensuous and uninhibited. So unlike the brittle, stiff-necked, tight-lipped ex-wife he'd met at the airport and then brought to his cabin.

He rubbed the back of his neck, wishing he could will away the valid reason Brynn had for her anger toward him. Laurel couldn't be willed away, though. He could wish that Brynn would forgive and forget how he had used her to replace his loss of Laurel, but could he honestly expect that much of her? Maybe not.

Hell. Standing in Brynn's shoes, he'd be pitiless and unforgiving, too. His own ego sure as sin had a sore spot named Laurel for the dump job she'd done on him. What Laurel had ever seen in slick-talking, swaggering rodeo promoter Cord Hayden, Flint still couldn't figure out.

Like Brynn, he knew the torture of coming in second when being first was the only prize. Still, Brynn had never been accustomed to placing first every time out, whereas he had never been anything less than a number one champion in those days. First in bronc riding, bull riding, steer roping; tops in prize earnings and endorsements; highest number of records broken.

Without knowing it, he'd been riding for a fall. Laurel had dealt him the losing blow a month after he retired to marry her.

Then, while he was impotent with rage and sodden with self-pity and tequila, Brynn had stepped in....

To the naked eye, she was Laurel in the flesh, and he hadn't been able to resist temptation. Addicted to being numero uno, he'd taken selfish advantage without thinking of consequences.

Thinking back on what an egotistical jerk he had been, Flint shook his head. He recalled Brynn sobering him up, murmuring to him, "Deep down inside, you're a better man than you appear to be."

Love, pure and simple, had been Brynn's only motive. His had been preserving his big ego—unfortunately, at her expense.

He liked to think he'd learned from his humbling mistakes and become the better man Brynn had seen in him long ago. Brynn didn't seem to think he'd improved since then. Nor did she seem to think she'd made any mistakes of her own in the past—like the mistake of confessing her secret love for him. And then the mistake of marrying him.

She could have said no when he proposed. God knows, he hadn't twisted her arm. He'd been decent enough to respect her virginity, too, and not ever tell her it was one physical difference between her and her twin. Laurel had been around, not that it mattered to him. Double standards didn't fit into his code of ethics, then or now.

Nonetheless, Brynn's inexperience had set her apart in at least one way from her sister. He'd had to be far more romantic with Brynn than with Laurel. He'd had to be careful, patient and reassuring. Somewhere in himself he had found those qualities at the time, enough that Brynn took to sex with him like a compass takes to true North.

He thought well of himself for that, if not for much else in his marriage to Brynn.

After the five years he'd had to regret past mistakes and improve himself, he felt sure he'd never regress and repeat them. Brynn couldn't see that he'd changed, but he could see change in himself.

He was starting to see that she'd changed, too, as he gazed down on her face. She seemed so different now, so . . . unusual. It was an inner quality, hard for him to quite identify, but there all the same.

Not a quality he associated with Laurel, not in any way. Brynn had become so much that she hadn't been before: a culinary professional; a wine sophisticate; a citizen of the world's favorite city. She'd also gotten married again and divorced again, and acquired two cats along the way.

Of course Flint had heard about Brynn's new life from her mom, Maggie, but there was a world of difference between hearing and seeing.

Much to his surprise, Brynn had become two women—a woman he already knew and a woman he'd never known.

As he was studying her, puzzling about her, becoming more than a little intrigued by her, she opened her eyes and caught him at it.

"What?" she murmured, blinking.

"Your morning coffee, ma'am," he improvised, setting his mug on the sofa arm. "You still like it black, no sugar?"

She nodded sleepily. "Thanks. What time is it?"

Time for my shower, he thought. Yet he postponed it, because watching Brynn yawn and stretch and wake to the morning was a sight he suddenly didn't want to miss.

"Around about eight-thirty," he replied.

Her fair, curly hair was enticingly mussed, and her heavy-lidded eyes had a smoky, lambent look that formed a sexy contrast to her prim, buttoned-up pajama top.

When had she started wearing pajamas? Or did she only have them for visits home? He was curious, he realized, more than he'd been about any woman in a mighty long time.

Brynn glanced around. "Oh, Matchmaker's here."

"Yep."

Flint made an effort not to stare openmouthed at the slow smile the sight of the doe brought to Brynn's full, pouty lips. His memory of kissing her was as fresh in his mind as if it had happened a few seconds ago rather than hours earlier. She had been so hot, so passionate, so . . .

He clipped the steamy thought short as Brynn sat up against her pillow. She took the mug and tasted the coffee.

"Mmm. Just what I need to perk me up."

Flint knew what *he* needed. That shower, fast. Still, he lingered, fascinated by his ex-wife's sleep-softened face and husky voice.

"I'm even going to cook you breakfast," he heard himself announce. Which was insane, because he had always been a kitchen klutz. Food rarely ever behaved for him. No, it mostly burned, boiled over, or ruined itself in any number of other ways whenever he tried to do something with it. Coffee was one of the few exceptions to that rule.

Breakfast. He could hardly believe his runaway mouth.

Brynn apparently couldn't, either, because she was staring over the rim of her cup at him as if he'd lost his IQ.

"Did you say what I thought you said?" she inquired.

Flint got a grip on himself. "Maybe not."

"That's a big relief."

"You don't mind doing the cooking again, Brynn?"

"No. I enjoy my life's work." She took a long sip from her mug. "Anyway, I've already got breakfast planned."

"What's the menu?"

She got out of the bed. "Wait and see. First, I need to wash my face, brush my teeth, all that. Then I'll cook while you take your shower."

Flint watched her stockinged feet hit the floor. He got himself another mug of coffee as she padded away to the bathroom with the one he'd given her.

Glad to expend some excess energy, he straightened the bed and tucked the bedclothes in tight. Brynn's pillow and the area where she had slept retained her body heat. Her scent floated up to him, evoking memories of being married to her and waking up with her every morning for six months.

Back then he had been able to open his eyes, gaze at his wife and think, *Laurel. Same face, hair, eyes, skin, height, weight, body shape.* What a self-centered damn fool he had been!

There was no way to make that up to Brynn. No sir. Nor any way for Brynn to deny that she had pretty much thrown herself at him for her own personal reasons at the weakest, unhappiest, most depressing time of his life.

In their own screwed-up ways, they'd taken advantage of each other. They'd be regretting it for the rest of their lives.

His thoughts were interrupted by Brynn's return to the main room. Putting the past out of his mind, he folded the bed into the sofa frame. Now for that shower he had coming. Damned if he'd wear his shirttails out all day.

"See you after all the hot water's used up," he told Brynn.

She called after him, "Save enough for washing the dishes."

Hearing the shower turn on, Brynn breathed a sigh of relief. She could get dressed now that Flint was out of the way. Then she'd make blueberry griddle cakes from the supply of canned fruit and biscuit mix in the cupboard. And all the while, she'd do her rock-bottom best to forget what had almost happened last night.

AFTER BREAKFAST, Flint shoveled a path in the snow between the cabin and the Bronco. Brynn listened to the radio while he worked, and learned that the highway was now clear.

When Flint finished, Matchmaker followed him and Brynn to and from the car as they packed Brynn's suitcases and the cats in the carriers, preparing to leave. The sun sent glorious light sparkling on fresh-fallen snow. A playful breeze fluffed the soft, powdery drifts. Hank, the neighbor, was out plowing the entry lane clear with his Snow Dozer.

A woman bundled up in a hooded snowsuit and snow boots emerged from the cabin next door, waving to Flint and Brynn with mittened hands.

"Hi," she called out. "Gorgeous day."

"Amelia," Flint informed Brynn. He greeted Hank's wife. "Howdy. Thanks for loaning us the cat stuff."

Amelia came over to them, smiling at Brynn. "Did your kitties like the food?"

"Better than what they get at home," Brynn replied. "I'll have to buy them your brand from now on."

Amelia was a plump, fiftyish woman whose china-blue eyes and freckled face radiated an open, homey friendliness. She pushed back her parka hood a few inches, revealing springy red hair.

Flint introduced her to Brynn, then went inside to get Amelia's cat box and kibble. Brynn opened the cargo door of the Bronco and showed off Mick and Minn in their carriers. Unhappy at being caged again, they meowed their displeasure.

Matchmaker stuck her head in, too, perhaps to commiserate with the cats or bid them goodbye. Flint came back out and returned Amelia's cat supplies.

"Thanks again." He glanced at Matchmaker, then raised his eyebrows at Amelia. "By the way, where can I adopt a tame deer like her?"

Amelia chuckled. "My, she made quite an impression on you."

Brynn said, "She made both of us fall in love with her."

"If you're not too attached to her," Flint said, "would you consider letting me adopt her?"

"Well, we *are* attached, Hank and I, but . . ." Amelia hesitated, frowning. "Our cat won't accept her. We've had Tigs eight years and Matchmaker only a month." She bit her lip. "We had no idea Tigs would flip out. He hardly touches his food, won't purr anymore, bares his fangs when she tries to make friends with him."

Brynn sympathized, "Poor Tigs."

"Let's see what Hank says," Amelia decided. "Here he comes."

Finished plowing, her husband had parked the Snow Dozer in his driveway and was approaching the Bronco. A broad, brawny man, he wore a shiny yellow snow slicker and rubber galoshes that squeaked on the snow.

Flint shook hands with him, introduced Brynn and then proposed to adopt Matchmaker.

"We'd miss her," Hank told him after a questioning glance at Amelia, "but Tigs sure wouldn't."

Flint said, "Tell you what. Let Matchmaker decide."

He cleared a space for her in the Bronco's hold and patted his hand on the empty spot. "Here, girl," he coaxed. "Want to come home with me? Hmm? Go for a nice long ride to my cattle ranch?"

To everyone's surprise, the dainty doe scrambled into the vehicle without any hesitation and made herself comfortable alongside the cat carriers. Mick and Minn instantly stopped complaining and set up loud purrs.

"There's our answer," said Hank.

Amelia nodded. "I'll sign her adoption form over to you, Flint. Just a sec." She hurried inside to get the document.

Flint took out a pen and checkbook. "Name your adoption fee, Hank."

"No fee, no sir." Hank shook his head. "Just give her a good home and lots of love. And bring her back to visit every now and then."

"My pleasure," Flint assured him. "You're invited to visit her at the ranch anytime, too."

Amelia returned with the adoption paper, looking both regretful and relieved. She and Hank bid the deer a fond farewell.

A few minutes later, Brynn waved goodbye to them as Flint drove the Bronco out of the lane to the highway.

Settling into her seat for the long ride ahead, she said to Flint, "You're still as impulsive as ever, aren't you?"

"In some ways, yep," he replied with a cocky grin. "In some other ways, uh-uh."

"A pet deer," she marveled wryly.

"She charmed me into it. And you were on my side, too, for a change." He mimicked her, "'Poor little Tigs.' I owe you for making up Amelia's mind right then and there."

Brynn reasoned, "We're even now, since I owe you for driving me home."

"You owe me more for this than a few words," he corrected.

She warned him, "I know what you're thinking."

"What?"

"Temporary cook."

"Well? Do I still have to take no for an answer?"

"Yes. Why do you keep bugging me about it?"

"Shoot, we were getting along so well there for about three seconds." He muttered a curse under his breath and began fiddling irritably with the temperature control.

Brynn crossed her legs and folded her arms. "I'll thank you to stop cussing, Flint."

"Maybe I will and maybe I won't," he drawled, tipping his Stetson low over his brows. "Tell you one thing for sure, though. You're not the sympathetic, kindhearted gal I once married. Not by a long shot."

Brynn retorted, "You're still the man *I* once married. You want your own way—only yours—first and foremost. You go any length to get it."

"The hell I do."

"The hell you don't."

"You're cussing now yourself, Brynn."

"I'm being pushed to it, Flint."

"Pushed, my eye. You haven't budged one bit about anything to do with me so far."

"Don't expect me to," she firmly assured him. "I've changed in one way, that's for sure. I'm not the pushover I used to be where you were concerned."

He argued, "You didn't *need* any pushing over back then. I never invited you over to sober me up after Laurel cut me low. You traipsed into my ranch house all on your own—didn't even knock beforehand."

"You were too drunk to answer your door, much less hear me knock," she fumed.

"A man's entitled to drink himself deaf after he gets chucked." He hunkered down behind the steering wheel and ground out another twice-as-offensive curse.

Brynn gritted her teeth, unable to imagine why she'd ever fallen in love with, much less married, this impossible man. She only knew, better than ever, how exceedingly brilliant she'd been to divorce him!

6

FLINT BROUGHT Brynn home by midmorning, without another word spoken between them along the way. Not a word at the rest room stops they made for themselves and the animals. Not a sound as the miles rolled by.

Flint finally broke the tense silence as he turned the Bronco into the long gravel driveway leading to Arch and Maggie McBride's ranch house. A scant six inches of snowfall blanketed the level sheep pastures on either side of the driveway. In the near distance, at a higher elevation, the snow-crowned crest of Wilder Butte rose against the clear sky.

"Might as well put a decent face on for your folks," he told Brynn.

She gave a brief nod of agreement without looking at him. "If they invite you in, beg off."

"Bug off, you mean."

"Listen, Flint, I appreciate your time and trouble in bringing me home. I thank you for that, all right?"

He returned her short nod. "All right, you're welcome. And I'll thank you not to issue me any high-and-mighty orders to beg off. Arch and Maggie are good friends to me, just as I'm a good friend to them. If they invite me in for coffee, well, I'm going to sit a friendly spell with them."

Flint saw from Brynn's obstinate expression that she didn't cotton to his words or his friendship with her parents.

When had she grown so stubborn and independent-minded, so resistant, so all-around maddening? And why, he'd like to know, did he find it so all-fired attractive? Worse than that, it was a turn-on. His inborn will to win, to have what he wanted, was cropping up too strong for comfort.

During the trip, he'd found himself thinking repeatedly, *If Brynn had been like this before she married me…*

The thought kept straying off, incomplete. He had no idea how things might stand today if Brynn had been one hell of a handful long ago, instead of softhearted and gullible to a fault.

Guilt sparred with the attraction he was feeling. He couldn't dismiss his memory of how sweet, shy, dreamy-eyed and romantic-hearted Brynn had been before. Too kind and trustful for her own good, and way too deep in love with him at the time. He had taken everything she offered and given her little in return beyond his name in marriage and pleasure in bed.

Flint brought the Bronco to a stop at the McBrides' rustic clapboard house. So much for his earlier aim of mending broken fences with Brynn, he thought. He'd brought his ex-wife home safe from Portland, but that was the extent of it. Nothing was patched up or even smoothed over a little, and he still hadn't brought himself higher than a pasture patty in Brynn's view of the past.

Seeing Archer and Maggie on the front porch, smiling with their three tail-wagging sheepdogs, he altered his expression to resemble theirs. No use spoiling Brynn's welcome home. She was pasting on a happy face, too, he noted, first time she'd smiled in hours.

A moment later he was caught up, after Brynn, in a warm hug from her lively, effusive mother. All around them, the dogs yipped and jumped. Arch clapped Flint's shoulder with a big, work-worn hand and thanked him profusely for fetching Brynn home. Flint demurred that it was no trouble at all, his pleasure, one social fib after another.

Then Maggie spotted Matchmaker. "What's that in the back of your—" Her snappy hazel eyes widened. "Oh, my goodness!"

The rough planes and crags of Arch's weathered face creased in curious disbelief. "What are you two doing with a Bambi in there?"

Brynn explained all about the deer as Flint opened up the Bronco's cargo door. Maggie and Arch ordered the dogs back to the porch and Matchmaker stepped out looking confident that there was nothing to fear.

Arch, an aging lion of a man, stood shaking his shaggy, gray-blond head. "Well, how do you do, big eyes?"

Matchmaker sniffed the hand he put out to her, then lightly licked it in greeting. She did the same to Maggie, who giggled with delight.

"She's practically as pretty as you," Arch teased Maggie, his gray eyes twinkling as he tousled his wife's short, gray hair.

Maggie pecked a kiss on his cheek and gave another delighted laugh.

They were so happy together, Flint thought, scuffing the toe of his boot in the gravel-packed snow of the driveway. Happy in a way he secretly feared he'd never be. Glancing up at Brynn, he saw the same yearning as his own pass over her face as she gazed at her loving parents. She caught his glance and looked away.

"Let's not forget Mick and Minn," she said. "They deserve equal time."

The two cats seemed to agree, both of them pawing at the grill wire on their carriers, trying to break through.

"Oh, they're cute as can be, Brynn," Maggie said, helping her lift out the travel cages. "I've got a privy box set up for them in the mudroom. Let's all go in to some hot coffee and a crumb cake fresh from the oven. Your favorite." She added briskly, "Flint's, too."

Toting Brynn's suitcases, the men followed the women, cats and Matchmaker to the porch. The three sheepdogs stayed sitting and obedient to orders, yet they didn't take their eyes off the animal menagerie entering the house.

Flint halted behind Brynn as she paused to greet each dog with a pat on the head. "Hi, Bozz. Hi, Pudge. Hi, Cleo." They all eyeballed the cat in the carrier she held.

Flint couldn't help eyeing her firm, rounded bottom as she bent and petted the dogs. He thought about how his hands had roved over her the night before, how warm and womanly she had been to his touch.

He drew a deep breath and reined in the sensual memory. Maybe he *should* beg off staying for coffee and crumb cake, since he couldn't seem to stop responding physically to Brynn. Or was it a holdover from the past, proof that he was still hooked on Brynn because she looked exactly like Laurel?

If he was, he wasn't aware of it on the surface. Laurel's name and his timeworn memories of her hadn't popped into his thoughts for hours, until he questioned himself just now. Yet, with identical twins, could he ever know for sure?

He had no business feeling this way, no matter how appealing Brynn had started to seem overnight. He wouldn't speak another word about her pinch-hitting as his cook, either. He didn't need to have Laurel's lookalike at Wilder Butte again if he couldn't trust himself to keep his cool.

Continuing inside after Brynn, Flint decided he'd skedaddle home as soon as good manners allowed. He wouldn't visit the McBride ranch again until Brynn's vacation was over.

Out of sight, he told himself, out of mind.

A few minutes later, he sat down at the kitchen table with Maggie and Arch. Brynn was in their guest room, freshening up after getting the cats situated. Matchmaker was with Mick and Minn, nosing around the house.

"Sorry we sent you off on a trip that ended up taking so long," Arch said.

Flint waved off the apology. "There's no predicting snowslides. Besides, I got the chance to check up on my little cabin. And the chance to adopt Matchmaker, too."

"How did she get her name?" Maggie asked.

"Forgot to ask," Flint replied. He shrugged. "Maybe she brought somebody together at the petting zoo where she lived before."

"Maybe she'll match up some of the single guests who stay at Wilder Butte," Maggie mused, as she poured coffee and served the spicy cake.

Arch gave his wife a playful pinch on the hip. "Romance, romance. All you women think about in your spare time."

"What spare time, you romantic old coot? I haven't had any since I've been cooking over at Flint's place." Maggie set the sugar bowl between the two men. "Not that we can't use my earnings from it, especially after adding up yesterday's vet bill."

Flint told them, "I asked Brynn if she'd fill in. She turned me down flat."

"I figured she might," Arch said, nodding and frowning at the same time.

Maggie sighed. "Flint, don't look for anyone else to fill in until I have a talk with her first. Okay?"

"She's dead set, Maggie." Flint cut into his crumb cake and wolfed down a big bite. "Ten to one she won't stop freshening herself up in there until I head on home."

"Oh, fudge." Maggie's shoulders slumped as she stirred cream into her coffee. "I hoped you two might bury the hatchet."

He shook his head, gulping coffee from his cup. "About all we agreed on was adopting that deer."

There was disappointed silence from Arch and Maggie. Flint was sorry to dampen their mood with the truth, but there it was, no use tenderfooting around it.

He made short work of the cake and the rest of his coffee.

"I'd better load up Matchmaker and hit the road home."

Apparently hearing her name, Matchmaker came to the kitchen doorway and fluttered her long eyelashes at him.

Maggie checked the wall clock. "I'll be over in an hour or so to start up lunch—sloppy joes this time."

"I'll pay you double today," Flint said, "for your extra trouble."

"What trouble?"

"You'd rather be home here visiting with Brynn than making lunch at my place. That's what."

Maggie's hazel eyes flashed at him. "Neighbors help neighbors out, Flint. Yesterday you enabled us to stay here and tend to our sick sheep. I won't take one penny extra for cooking today, period."

"Now, Maggie—"

"Son," Arch interrupted, "just do yourself a favor and say 'yes, ma'am' whenever she gets that look in her eye. I learned long ago it means give up without a fight."

Flint smiled. "Whatever you say, ma'am." He pushed his chair back and stood up. "Thanks for the fine crumb cake."

The McBrides left the kitchen with him and Matchmaker. On the way to the front door, Maggie called out to Brynn, "Flint's leaving."

Flint wasn't surprised to hear only silence in reply as he led Matchmaker outside. He figured Brynn was thinking, *Good riddance to him!*

"I'll have a talk with her," Maggie repeated, while he stowed Matchmaker in the Bronco.

Flint advised her, "Don't waste your breath. It's probably best this way for Brynn and me—keeping out of each other's way." He swung into the driver's seat. "Adios, Arch. See you before lunch, Mag."

"YOU WOULDN'T EVEN SAY goodbye, Brynn?"

Brynn looked at her mother standing in the doorway of the guest room. "I said my goodbyes to Flint when I left to divorce him, Mom."

Maggie came in and sat down on the bed with Mick and Minn, who were watching Brynn unpack suitcases. "I've never seen you act so vindictive and hardhearted. You aren't like this toward Kelly Reilley."

"Flint and Kelly are two different breeds of men," Brynn replied. "Kelly is a soft, cuddly teddy bear. Flint is . . ."

"A man," Maggie stated. "The real thing."

Brynn argued, "He's one big hotheaded ego, as self-centered and self-serving as ever. He doesn't want *me*—he wants a cook! He didn't marry *me*, he married—"

She stopped her sudden tirade and bit her lip, feeling too much as if she might burst into tears.

"Honey, come here." Maggie held out her arms. "I know what happened and why. Come cry it all out and have it done with, at least for a little while."

Battling tears that threatened to spill over, Brynn breathed out a ragged sigh and sank down next to her mother. Maggie's cradling arms were a refuge Brynn couldn't resist.

"It still hurts, Mom," she admitted. "So much."

Maggie stroked her daughter's shoulder comfortingly. "Yes. You loved Flint with all your heart."

Brynn let the teardrops fall. "I loved Kelly, too, but not the same."

"You married him to deny your deeper love for Flint," Maggie murmured.

"I've been so foolish, Mom. Twice."

"You've been human, Brynn, that's all. I'm glad Armand made you take some time off."

Brynn grimaced, wiping her cheeks with the back of one hand. "I'm lucky he didn't fire me. All those salty soups and lumpy sauces, day after day."

Maggie gave a gentle chuckle and they sat there together for a while, petting the cats, restoring emotional equilibrium.

Then Brynn said, "You've been so worried about Dad, but I can't see why. He looks healthy, strong, happy."

Maggie twirled Minn's fluffy tail around one finger. "I know what you mean. You'd never guess I caught him having another dizzy spell the other day in one of the sheep sheds."

Brynn grimaced. "How many have there been?"

"Four that I've witnessed myself so far. He shook me off about the last one and tried to act normal. I worry about him all the time I'm over at Flint's, I tell you. If something happened to Arch all alone over here, who would know but the sheep?"

"Dad still won't go to the doctor, then?"

"No, even though I nag him morning, noon and night. A word from you added to mine might change his mind."

Brynn mused grimly, "He's as mule minded about doctors as Flint is about wanting me to cook at Wilder Butte."

"Honey, it worries Flint to know I'm worried about Arch. Flint feels guilty for needing me to cook until his new chef can start." Maggie paused meaningfully. "He feels guilty for hurting you, too."

Brynn closed her tear-swollen eyes. "He doesn't know it still hurts after all this time."

"He knows how his own past wounds from Laurel feel, healed up though I suspect they are," Maggie countered. "I'm not defending his part in hurting you, but you set yourself up for it against the advice Arch and I gave you to let Flint grieve alone over losing Laurel."

"Now I wish I had listened." Brynn sighed regretfully.

Maggie went on, "My advice to you now is to help me out by cooking the next week or so at Wilder Butte. Flint wasn't being self-serving to ask you. He was hoping to make things easier on me."

"I'd be happy to help you out, Mom. Flint didn't phrase it that way when he asked, though."

"Men." Maggie rolled her eyes. "They can't communicate worth a hoot half the time." She got up, brisk and lively again. "When do you want to start stirring up Flint's pot? I'll drive you the three miles over there."

"Lunch seems like a good start," Brynn said, trying to match her mom's energetic tone. "Today."

Maggie beamed. "Thank you, honey, from the bottom of my heart. You won't regret it."

FLINT WAS ON the kitchen phone at Wilder Butte Ranch, trying to find a stand-in cook, when Maggie and Brynn walked in together. He almost dropped the receiver, seeing Brynn.

"Hold the line a minute," he told the emergency employment agency he'd called.

Maggie hiked a thumb at her daughter. "My replacement, Flint, beginning today."

"How'd *that* happen?"

Brynn snapped her fingers. "The old-fashioned way. Family ties."

Flint turned back to the phone and told the party on the line, "Sorry I bothered you. I've finally got my big problem fixed here. Adios."

He hung up, blinking at Brynn. "What changed your mind?"

"What difference does it make?" Brynn replied as she and her mother took off their coats.

"I'd just like to know."

"Flint, I'm ready to take this job off Mom's hands at the same rate you're paying her. That's all that matters."

He went into a teasing mode. "Was it anything I said? Bet it was."

"If you want lunch served on time today, stop asking trite questions and move out of our way."

Flint looked from her to her mother and then grinned. "Yes, ma'ams." He jammed his hat on his head. "You need me for anything in the meantime, I'm out in the saddle shop."

Watching him swagger from the kitchen with his thumbs hooked in his belt loops, Brynn muttered to

Maggie, "You'd think he personally had everything to do with changing my mind."

"You mean he didn't?" Maggie inquired with wry, mock surprise. "You're only doing it for dear old Mom?"

"For you, Mom, I'd do anything. For him, only sloppy joes."

"That's the spirit, Brynn." Maggie waved a hand at the spacious, rustic kitchen. "It hasn't changed any since you lived here."

Brynn looked around at the pine countertops and roomy cupboards, the eight-burner range and the commercial-size fridge, the stout oak worktable centered in the room.

She had once been Flint's wife here, cooking meals in this kitchen. Here, to his big rambling ranch house, she had come as Flint's bride with dreams of sharing his life and being happy with him. Dreams that had never come true for her or for him—girlish, romantic dreams she should never have had . . .

The old, gracious house held so many memories. She felt an inner need to reminisce, painful though it would be, but not with Maggie there. Later, perhaps, when no one was around.

Shaking off the remembrance, she asked her mother, "How many are there for lunch today?"

"Ten, excluding ourselves." Maggie started counting off the ranch employees first. "The foreman, the same three wranglers as before, a cross-country ski guide for the guests, and Flint, of course. The house-maid lives in but she fixes her own lunch, since she's always on one fad diet after another. Her sister takes her place on days off."

Brynn was surprised to hear Flint had a foreman now. Maggie explained that he'd hired Roper Slocum a couple of years ago to supervise Jed, Owen and Carlos, the cowhands Brynn remembered from before.

"Having Roper gives Flint more time to design saddles," Maggie added. "Extra time to teach me leather working, too."

"How many guests are here?"

"Four right now—two married couples. Tomorrow a bachelor arrives."

Listening to Maggie, Brynn heard a man speak from the back kitchen door. "What's this I hear about a new cook, Mrs. Mags?"

Maggie smiled over Brynn's shoulder. "Roper. Come meet my daughter, Brynn. I'm telling her what a big help you are to Flint."

Brynn turned and saw a man of her father's age giving her a wide, toothy smile. He swept off his weather-stained Stetson and revealed a balding scalp that was a pale contrast to his sparse, ginger brown hair and the leathery, tanned skin of his kindly face. His shearling jacket, worn jeans and scuffed boots clothed a wiry body built for hard work in the outdoors.

He put out a callused hand to her when Maggie introduced him. "Mornin', Brynn. I've heard a bit about you from your mama. And a littler bit from your ex-husband."

Brynn shook his hand, unsure how to respond.

"I'll be cooking from now until the new chef can take over," she finally commented.

"Glad to have you." He raised his eyebrows at Maggie. "Thought you were here for a while longer."

Maggie shook her head. "Not after today. With Brynn stirring the pots now, you'll all eat a lot better and I'll catch up on my own work at home."

"Been eating real good all along," Roper assured her diplomatically. He started backing up to leave. "See ya when the lunch bell rings, Ms. Brynn. My boys'll be starved as usual."

Brynn nodded. "I remember how much they used to put away at every meal. Especially Owen. Is he still a bottomless pit?"

"Worse than you recall, probably." Roper's dark eyes twinkled. "Him and his tapeworm."

Roper settled his hat on his head and went back outside.

"The nicest possible man," said Maggie after he'd gone. "Flint met him way back during the rodeo days. As you might expect from his nickname, his claim to rodeo fame was lasso tricks."

No sooner had the foreman left than a Hispanic woman came bustling into the kitchen through the dining room. Plump and sturdy, with silvered black hair worn in a thick plait down her back, the maid was humming pleasantly to herself.

Seeing Brynn with Maggie, she stopped short. "*Hola.* Your daughter, *sí, señora?*"

"*Sí, señora,*" Maggie affirmed, and introduced Brynn to Constanza Rios, the housemaid.

"Brynn," Constanza repeated after Maggie. "The wife of Señor Flint many years ago," she stated as matter-of-factly as Roper had.

"Yes, I was," Brynn said, wishing she didn't have a history that preceded her.

It wasn't any surprise that everyone knew everyone else's business, past and present, at Wilder Butte. Since few things remained hidden for very long among people in rural communities, there could be no anonymity for her here, as there was in San Francisco.

Here, she was one of Archer and Margaret Mc-Bride's identical twins, the twin whom Flint Wilder had married after the other twin jilted him. Brynn would always be the wife who hadn't stayed married to him beyond six months.

Constanza gave Brynn a brief, warm welcome, then bustled away to begin laying out the dining room table for lunch.

"Where are the guests?" Brynn asked Maggie.

"One of the couples was planning to sightsee in Bend for most of the morning. The other couple said something about going for a cross-country ski tour with the guide. The snow trail up on the butte is perfect."

Maggie went on to say that the couples were booked for two weeks at Wilder Butte, as was the bachelor who would arrive tomorrow.

Brynn started peeling and dicing the onions. Watching her, Maggie sighed. "You do that just like the chefs on TV. Ten times faster than I can."

"Nothing to it," Brynn quipped.

But, of course, there was intensive training behind her chopping technique. Mastering that and her other culinary skills had taken time, concentrated study and commitment. Brynn was proud of being a professional now, proud enough to show off a little to her mother.

"My daughter the hotel chef," Maggie said, beaming with motherly pride. She took several pounds of ground beef from the refrigerator and brought out burger buns from the pantry. "Shall I stay and help you cook this meal?"

"No, I'll wing it, Mom. You go on home and keep an eye on Dad."

"He needs one kept on him," Maggie declared as she put her coat back on. "Call just before you're ready to come home and I'll come get you."

Brynn asked, "What were you going to make for dinner here tonight?"

"*Fajitas*, both beef and chicken. Thanks a million again, honey."

"Don't mention it." Brynn waved the knife at her playfully. "Get on home. I'll find everything I need as I go along here."

"More than you expect, perhaps," Maggie murmured, then stepped out before Brynn could ask her what she meant by that comment.

Brynn concluded that Maggie still had hopes that Brynn and Flint would someday let bygones be bygones. *Not any day soon, Mom*, Brynn mentally informed her. *Not until my love for Flint dies out, which isn't likely.*

At that thought, Brynn felt tears sting her eyes but she held them back and laid the blame for them on the chopped onions. She'd be a wreck if she let herself reminisce. Instead, she focused her thoughts on work.

Constanza could be heard humming in the adjacent dining room as she set out plates and silverware. It was a cozy, cheery, infectious sound that eventually buoyed

Brynn's spirits. Before long, Brynn was humming too, feeling less downcast and more at home in Flint's house than she really should allow herself to feel.

It would be much too easy to pretend that she was his wife again.

And much too foolish.

7

LUNCH WENT OFF ON TIME and received rave reviews.
Afterward, Brynn got acquainted with Constanza,
who'd served the meal. As they cleaned up the kitchen
together, Brynn learned that Constanza was in her late
fifties, a widow whose only child was grown and married. Brynn learned, too, that Constanza was one very
candid, forthright woman who didn't hesitate to ver-
balize her thoughts.

"Señor Flint has his eyes on you," said the maid.

"Not on me," Brynn told her. *My sister, yes. Me, no*.

"Oh, yes," Constanza insisted. "He has a gleam for
you. I noticed it during lunch." She sighed. "A lonely
man he is. He needs a wife like you.

"I've been his wife, as you know," Brynn said.

Constanza nodded. "I know very well, because I am
a very nosy and romantic person." She gave a mirthful
grin, then cocked one ear to the dining room door. "I
hear him coming to flirt with you."

Flint stepped in a moment later, but not to flirt. He
brusquely asked her to come into his office, which was
near the kitchen, down a short hall. Puzzled, she
shrugged and followed him in. She found the office the
same as it had been five years ago, furnished with a
burl-wood desk and leather chairs. Indian rugs cov-

ered the oak floor and collections of arrowheads decorated the walls.

Brynn took a seat in one of the chairs opposite his desk. Flint closed the door and then sat down in his high-backed desk chair.

He stared at her for a moment. "How did you make sloppy joes taste like beef bourguignonne?" he asked, shaking his head in wonder.

She shrugged. "I added bacon, red wine, thyme. A little of this and that. Why?"

"I figure I owe you more now than what I paid your mom."

"For what?"

"The food. Maggie's a good, basic cook," he replied, "no doubt about it. But that lunch you just put out was melt-in-my-mouth fantastic."

Brynn looked pleased by his high praise, Flint thought. She didn't look willing to accept higher pay, however. Her arms were folded across her middle, a sure sign that she was going to argue.

"I stated my terms when I arrived earlier with Mom, Flint."

He objected, "Maggie doesn't have to know, if it's her feelings you're worried about."

"I'm doing my mother a favor. I refuse to benefit from it."

Flint felt a strong urge to lift her up by her stiffly set shoulders and kiss her into submitting to his will. She was driving him more than a little crazy by being so changed from the submissive Brynn he remembered.

"You refuse everything that comes from me, Brynn."

She started to rise, saying, "I have to clean up in the kitchen."

"Not until we settle our differences in here," he retorted forcefully enough that she settled back down again. "If you don't want the pay your cooking deserves, quit cooking so all-fired well."

Her arms folded again, tighter. "Lower my professional standards? I can't do that."

"Take what you're worth, then. Lord Almighty, why is everything between us a wrangle?"

"You always want your own way," she replied.

He countered, "If you ask me, you want yours even worse."

He sat in silence for a moment, returning her cool glare, seeing if she'd blink and back down. She showed no sign of giving way to him.

"Helping Mom is the only reason I'm here, as I've already said."

"Well, I'll help her then, too, and balance the pay scale at the same time by letting you use my Bronco to go the three miles back and forth from here to home. That'll save her or your dad doing it."

He retrieved his extra key and held it out to Brynn. She gave it such a hesitant look, he thought about changing his mind.

He'd already debated with himself about giving Brynn the key. Having her own transportation would be much more convenient. On the other hand, the more hassle there was for her and her folks, the more she might consider lodging in the cook's room. If that happened, the sooner the better, he was thinking.

He had a vision of relaxing by the fire with Brynn in the late evening after a long day. Learning more about her. Gaining her trust, her goodwill. Earning some forgiveness, some redemption.

Along with his vision came vivid, arousing memories of the physical passion he and Brynn had put into the six months of their marriage. There hadn't been anything that passionate for him since then. He'd gotten a tempting, tantalizing taste of it again last night in bed with Brynn. Too much of a taste not to crave more every time he looked at her now.

As much as he desired to have her around, he knew it would be selfish not to share the Bronco with Brynn.

He kept holding the key out to her. "I don't need it much day to day in the wintertime."

Brynn hesitated a moment more, then took the key. "It won't inconvenience you?"

"Nope. I can always borrow Roper's pickup, or one from the hands, if I need wheels unexpectedly."

"All right. Thank you, Flint."

"My pleasure." And it was, to see her mouth soften in a smile. He sat back in his chair, studying her. "We've got a couple of other things to get straight while we're at it."

Looking less resistant, Brynn unfolded her arms and clasped her hands in her lap. "What other things?"

"Where you'll be staying, for one. The cook's room is yours if going home between meals gets tiresome for you."

"I'll see how I feel after a few days," she said. "What else?"

"Us. The cold war between us."

"Not much can be done about that, all things considered," she murmured, looking down at her hands.

He replied, "Why not, since everybody is friendly with everybody else here? Besides, I don't like battling all the time with you."

He had mixed feelings about how stimulated he kept getting during every battle with her. It had a lot going for it in terms of sexual incitement; it had far less going for it in terms of peaceful living. Calling some sort of halt to the arguments might put him on an even keel about Brynn.

She kept her eyes on her clasped hands, as if she needed to contemplate every word he'd spoken. Looking at her, he was struck anew by how lovely she was, how lush and full her lips were, how curvy—and sexy—she looked in her plain white bibbed apron.

It seemed impossible, somehow, that Brynn had once been his wife or that he'd ever made love to her before. She wasn't the same woman, now, despite his previous familiarity with her. He knew her, yet didn't know her, an unnerving paradox for him.

Her wide-set gray eyes looked up from her hands and met his gaze. "I don't like our pitched battles any more than you do, Flint."

"So?" he questioned.

"So, maybe a cease-fire might work during the time I'm here."

"Shouldn't be all that hard to keep if we both do our best," he said.

"It won't be easy, either," she maintained, "considering the past."

"We're not looking backward from now on, okay?"

She nodded. "I'll give it a try."

"Brynn, if I could go back and change the wrong I did you, I would. Believe me, I would."

She gave another nod. "I'd change what happened, too, including—" she hesitated "—my own mistakes."

Flint was encouraged to hear Brynn say for once that she shared some of the fault. He didn't feel any the less blameworthy, but it made him feel a touch better.

She made a move to rise. "Is that all?"

"Not quite. Before you take full charge of the Bronco, I need it to do some errands in Bend today. You'd best come along and get whatever groceries you need for the next several meals."

"All right," she said. "I'll take inventory and make a list. Anything else?"

"Nothing more."

She left his office door open on her way out and Flint wondered what had gotten into him as he watched her go. He hadn't intended any drive into Bend until the moment the words popped out of his mouth.

Instead of keeping a friendly distance from Brynn, he was apparently dying to be alone with her again, all the way to Bend and back again. Something about his ex-wife was beginning to be too damned irresistible to him.

Too much for your own good and hers, he warned himself. But then he heard Brynn start humming as she went about tidying the kitchen. She sounded upbeat, optimistic, as if the idea of going to Bend with him appealed to her more than she'd wanted to show a few minutes ago.

It gave him hope that her heart might be softening toward him. Hope enough that he wasn't going to change his mind about driving fifty miles into Bend and the same distance back.

He was looking forward to it. A lot. And from the sound of things in the kitchen, he mused, maybe Brynn was, too.

BRYNN'S RIDE INTO BEND with Flint was agreeable, at least on the surface. They made light conversation along the way in a mutual effort to sustain the truce they'd agreed on earlier.

There remained a strong undercurrent of tension, however, since their grievances against each other still stood between them. Only for the time being was the past set aside, at least in Brynn's mind.

She felt there would never be any resolution, not so long as she continued to love Flint. She grudgingly admitted to herself that fighting her love for him was useless. It was there, centered in her heart, no matter how much she wished otherwise.

She must live with it—and hide it to save her own pride.

Flint dropped her off at a discount outlet in Bend, then drove on to run his own errands.

In the store, Brynn was surprised to find that the manager was an old high school classmate of hers. Randle Fowler had matured from a gangly, gawky, carrot-topped adolescent into something of a hunk with dark red hair and a flirtatious grin.

Brynn didn't recognize Randle on sight, but he identified her right away as a McBride twin. He asked the inevitable question.

"Which one are you?"

"Brynn."

He snapped his fingers. "The quiet one. Right. I heard a rumor you moved to San Francisco. True?"

"True."

He meandered up and down the aisles with her, trading notes on past and present, as she filled a flatbed cart with food and kitchen supplies. Along the way, she learned that he'd had a short marriage that had ended in divorce. No children.

His eyebrows went up when she told him she was cooking at Flint's ranch. "I thought you divorced Wilder."

"I did. I'm only cooking there for the next week or so. Nothing more."

"Then maybe I could ask you for a date?" Randle winked engagingly.

Though flattered by his attention, Brynn wasn't all that interested in a date. She tried to let him down gently.

"Cooking three meals a day for a dozen people—plus visiting my parents—won't leave me much time."

He gave her his business card. "If you find a few hours you'd like to fill, phone me up."

Before Brynn could reply, Randle's name was paged over the sound system. He excused himself and hurried away. Brynn glanced at his card, then put it into her coat pocket.

She continued shopping while she debated whether some casual time out with Randle might be enjoyable and entertaining. He certainly seemed nice, and interested.

Would going out with him take her mind off Flint?

She turned a corner and saw Flint coming toward her, almost as if her merest thought of him had caused him to materialize. He was wearing his usual boots, jeans, gingham shirt and denim jacket. Intense and piercing below the brim of his hat, his gaze held hers as he approached. Brynn felt her heart start to skip beats. She suddenly had the strangest, most breathtaking impression that Flint was striding forward to claim her as his own, take her in his arms and . . .

He slid his hands into his front pockets when he reached her. "Spent all my money yet?"

"I've almost reached the end of my list," she replied, dismissing her strange impression. "You're back sooner than I expected."

"Nothing took long." He drew his hands out of his pockets and took the handle of the flatbed cart she had loaded with groceries. Pushing it ahead of him, he moved down the aisle with her.

"Finding everything on your checklist?"

She nodded. "So far, so good."

"Who were you jawing with when I got back?"

Brynn realized he must have seen her talking with Randle. "Someone who went to my high school. Why?"

Flint tipped his hat lower over his brow. "Just curious."

Brynn thought Flint looked more than curious; jealous was more like it. It came as a surprise to her. Unless this situation was reminding him of Laurel, who had been quite a flirt.

"You mind telling me who he is?"

"No, but what concern is it of yours?"

"I don't like his looks. Especially not the way he was looking you up and down."

"He was not."

"I could see it clear across the store, Brynn. What does he want you to do with his card?"

"Who do you think you are to ask, Flint?"

Flint subsided into silence. Uneasy, disturbing silence. "I guess I've got no right," he finally replied, "but maybe I wish I did."

Brynn stopped in midstep and stared at him. "You what?"

"Well, what would you do if I handed you *my* calling card? Would you tuck it in your pocket like you did his card, or would you pitch mine in the trash?"

She was too caught off guard by his words to reply, much less to grasp what he seemed to be implying. As she struggled to comprehend, Flint scowled.

"You'd probably pitch it, the way you're staring at me. Like I'm crazy or worse."

"You aren't making a great deal of sense."

"You could at least answer my question, Brynn."

"What—exactly—are you asking?"

His blazing eyes held hers as he slowly reached both hands out and gripped her shoulders. "I wish I knew. Everything I say to you turns out to be a big mistake. You'll never have any more use for me, will you?"

"I—" She couldn't continue, for he was pulling her closer, up against his hard, warm body. Right there in the middle of the warehouse aisle. Passing shoppers slowed down and gave them curious looks.

"Brynn, don't you have any good feelings left for me? Not even a few?"

"I'm—" Self-preservation warned against telling him the truth, but deceit had never been her strongest suit. "I'm not sure."

"That makes two of us unsure whether you'll ever give me the time of day again." He tipped her chin up.

She moistened her lips, bit down into the lower one. "What are you getting at, Flint?"

"I'm curious, Brynn. How dead set are you against me?" His eyes searched hers, candid and compelling.

Brynn was aware that his hold on her, although firm, was not a restraint. She could easily step back away from him, if she really wanted to. She should, to prevent him from thinking she wanted anything to do with him.

"Maybe you're not a hundred percent against me," he suggested huskily. "You haven't hollered at me to bug off yet."

"I'm getting ready to," she warned him, making a move to pull free and keep her own distance. Staying close to him wasn't sensible or appropriate to the time, the place, or her own well-being. It was irresistible, though.

His grip tightened, holding her still. "How dead set? Give me a straight answer."

Reluctantly she admitted, "Maybe not a hundred percent."

"How much, then?"

"Why, Flint?"

"Hell if I know for sure," he said, then paused hesitantly. "Unless there's more going on between the two of us than meets the naked eye."

She searched his eyes for certainty, but could see only a complex mix of surprise and speculation. And self-deception, too?

"I seriously doubt that anything's going on," she told him.

Brynn almost took a step back, but Flint stopped her with his words.

"Want to bet?"

He dipped his head and placed a soft, gentle, persuasive kiss on her lips. Unable to resist for a long moment, she closed her eyes and surrendered to what she wanted so very much—a taste of the man she loved, would always love, couldn't afford to love.

He murmured against her lips, "What do you doubt about that, Brynn?"

"Ev-everything." She pulled out of his grip, turned away from him and found herself facing several shoppers who had stopped to watch. One of them, an older man, spoke up.

"Say, aren't you Flint Wilder? Rodeo?"

"That's me," Flint replied, after an uneasy glance at Brynn. "Retired."

The man grinned and whipped out a ballpoint pen. "Would you mind giving me your John Henry?"

"Mind? Where do I sign?"

Instantly, everyone else wanted autographs, too.

Embarrassed by the compromising scene she'd gotten into with Flint, and glad to be crowded out of the limelight, Brynn edged away with the grocery cart. Leaving Flint to a growing group of admirers, she found an out-of-the-way aisle where she paused to collect herself and ponder Flint's words and actions.

What if it meant he was becoming truly interested in her? What if it was only sexual attraction? Impulse, she tried to remind herself, was Flint's middle name—he wanted what he wanted when he wanted it, usually on the spur of the moment. Like staying at the ski cabin, adopting Matchmaker, signing up the first fill-in cook who crossed his path.

Could she—should she—let herself believe he'd been jealous about Randle? Or that he'd meant anything by questioning her, and then kissing her?

Yesterday, she would have said absolutely not. This morning she would have said the same thing. Now, not that much later, she had no answer to her own question.

She couldn't believe she was even asking it. Flint's words and one sweet, searching kiss had thoroughly confused her. She felt dazed, disconcerted, out of breath. She wasn't collecting her thoughts or making any real sense of what had happened.

Plagued with insecurity and self-doubt, she pushed the cart to a checkout line and paid for the groceries.

Flint caught up with her as she was steering the cart outside to the Bronco.

"Sorry I got ambushed so long," he apologized, taking charge of the cart from her. "Rodeo butts in at the damnedest times."

Brynn said, "You enjoy having the spotlight on you. You always did."

"Not half as much now as I used to, Brynn. I've changed a little more than you might think." He unlocked the passenger door. "Get in out of the cold. I'll stow this stuff in the back."

She watched him in the visor mirror and studied his expression as he loaded the groceries. He looked intent and meditative. He also looked rugged and so handsome . . . so capable of doing her harm.

Brynn closed her eyes, recalling his words. *What would you do if I handed you my calling card?* She relived the captivating moments when he'd kissed her. . .the enchanting pressure of his lips, the moist heat of his breath.

Flint got into the driver's seat. "Sleepy, Brynn?"

"Yes," she fibbed, keeping her eyes shut. Pretending to doze off would be easier than making awkward conversation.

The less said, the better. She was too confused as it was.

Flint drove the Bronco out of the lot and Brynn faked a nap all the way back to Wilder Butte.

8

HEADING UP THE MILE-LONG driveway to his ranch, Flint glanced over at Brynn in the passenger seat. He'd caught on that her nap was a charade, but he hadn't said a word.

If she wanted to shut him out because of what he'd said and done at the discount store, well, he could more than half understand why. He'd grabbed her, interrogated her and then planted a big one on her—right out in public where everyone could see. All the maturity he'd gained during the past five years had gone straight out the window the instant he saw Brynn with that other man.

A fine how-de-do. Jealous of another man. No right in the world to be jealous, either.

She was free to do as she pleased, go wherever she liked, have her social life any way she wanted it. It wasn't his place to interfere, question her and growl about it—except that he'd once been her husband, she'd once been his wife, and maybe in his mind that still counted for something.

It hadn't counted back when he heard about her second marriage. Rather than feeling possessive, he had hoped Brynn would be happy with Kelly Reilley, even though her own folks hadn't been hopeful at all about it.

But now, he had a different attitude developing toward Brynn and his present relationship to her. For reasons he couldn't explain to himself, he didn't want other men snaring her attention.

He wanted to capture it all himself, which she wasn't making easy for him. It made him all the more interested in her. Attracted to her. Fascinated, intrigued and frustrated by her.

"Brynn." He reached over and touched her shoulder. "We're getting close to home."

She opened her eyes, straightened up in her seat and covered a phony yawn behind one hand. Flint hid a smirk. The new Brynn was a wily woman who could rarely be caught in an unguarded moment.

Where she had once been guileless and eager to please, she was enigmatic and self-directed now. She had become unpredictable, too, a trait he himself possessed and found hard to control. Hell, he had no more idea of what she'd do next than what he would do in response.

He was getting hooked on something about her, red-hot for it, practically overnight. All it could mean was trouble, though he couldn't say he didn't like the challenge of pursuit. He couldn't say how he was going to handle it, either.

"I think I'll go home for an hour or so after I put the groceries away and prep for dinner," she said, checking her wristwatch after faking another yawn.

Flint shrugged, not eager for her to leave Wilder Butte where he could keep an appreciative eye on her. "What's the menu tonight?"

"Beef and chicken *fajitas*, with all the trimmings. Sangria for any wine drinkers, and pineapple short-cakes for dessert."

He whistled appreciatively. "Olé."

Brynn gave him the smile he was trying to pry out of her. "It's all quick and easy."

"Easy or not, it's still worth more than I'm paying you, Brynn."

"We argued that issue already, Flint. I won, remember?"

Flint nodded without enthusiasm. "What about the issue we argued at the store in Bend? You think you won that one, too?"

"Let's hope so," she murmured, turning her head away to look out the side window. "You weren't making a bit of sense."

"Why should I? You never give any credit to what I say anyway."

"I don't see any reason to."

"You see every reason not to."

"This argument you're starting is a fine way to maintain a truce, Flint."

"It would be easier if you were the same Brynn you used to be," he said. "You look the same but you've changed a lot otherwise."

Brynn kept her head turned away from him and murmured, "I look the same? The same as Laurel, right?"

"Back to that again," he griped.

She retorted, "If you were an identical twin, you'd know how it feels."

He shot back, "In my shoes, you might have reacted the same way I did. Ever think of it like that?"

Her silence told him she couldn't—or wouldn't—put herself in his place. Never did; never would.

Clenching his jaw in frustration, Flint parked the Bronco close to the kitchen door. He warned her, "I flat won't argue about who unloads this vehicle. So hold your fire about doing any part of it."

As she yanked open her door, she replied, "After winning two arguments today, I've got my quota."

Flint strode after her into the kitchen. "One win is all you can rightly claim." He caught her wrist and whirled her around to face him. "I didn't kiss you for no reason at all at that discount store, whatever you might think."

He wanted to kiss her again, feel her lips respond to his again. Although it was a need too new and unfamiliar for him to understand fully, *Brynn* was the stimulus, he knew that.

"Flint, kissing me whenever and wherever isn't going to put forgiveness in my heart for you...." Her tone broke and her words trailed away.

"You don't know what was in my mind, Brynn. Sure, I want to make up for the past, but that wasn't my intention in Bend. I—"

She cut him off with a pleading look. "You've got no right to kiss me at the drop of a hat. Isn't it enough that I never want to be hurt by you again?"

Sobered by a flash of raw pain in Brynn's eyes, he released her arm. "Enough? It's a bigger burden than I can live with," he ruefully replied. "You won't forgive me, won't accept my apologies. Whatever else I need from you, I can't seem to get."

He turned to go outside and unload the Bronco. Brynn's voice stopped him at the door.

"I'd bury the hatchet if I could, Flint."

He turned back to her, studied her expression and found it wary, uncertain, irresolute.

"You've already got my apologies," he said a little more gently. "Sealed with a kiss or two."

She gave a slight shrug. "Or three."

"You reacted with interest every time," he observed with a teasing smile.

Brynn didn't take issue with his words. His tone suggested she couldn't deny the truth of his assessment.

He toughened his smile into a brash grin and asked, "Will I get my shins kicked the next time?"

"There'd better not be one," she warned.

He backed out of the door, taunting, "With me, you never know, do you?"

He'd said enough, he reflected as he opened up the Bronco to unload it. Maybe too much. Without any forethought to speak of, as usual.

He wished now that it was more in his nature to calculate his moves before he made them, and clarify his thoughts before putting them into words. He wouldn't have become a rodeo champion by being careful and cautious, but life beyond the arena required less of the gut-instinct reactions that came so naturally to him.

Back in the kitchen with his first box of groceries, he took out a gallon jar of waffle syrup, six dozen bagels, a waxed round of cheddar cheese and another of mozzarella.

"That's *my* job," she said, watching his movements with a wary but close attention he found flattering.

He handed her a package of bagels. "I'll set the stuff out, you put it away." Whatever he had to do to stay around her a while longer.

She took the package, brushing her fingers against his in what seemed like slow motion. A little too lengthy for him to think it was accidental. It made him want her to touch him again at much greater length. Maybe she would, if another opportunity came her way.

Next he handed Brynn the syrup. Her fingers touched his again. An unnecessary, almost drawn-out, electrifying contact.

Flint drew in a deep breath to restrain a swell of intense, urgent desire for her. "I'll bring in the rest of the boxes."

Going out, he felt like a fool. By sharing the Bronco with her, he'd made it impossible to have any late nights by the fire with Brynn.

The more he wanted her, the harder she was to get.

MATCHMAKER WAS NOSING around the Bronco when Brynn went out to drive home after lunch. The sky was clear, the sun halfway to the western horizon. Brynn could see the vapor of her own breath and Matchmaker's in the cold, crisp air.

"Hi, girl." Brynn petted the doe's head with a mittened hand. "How do you like Wilder Butte so far?"

Matchmaker fluttered long eyelashes and gently butted her nose against Brynn's hand. Brynn marveled again at how trusting, docile and affectionate the little deer was. Everyone at the ranch was already smitten with her, ranch employees and guests alike.

Even Flint's pack of cow dogs had accepted her as an addition to the cattle, horses, chickens and barn cats they lived in harmony with.

"I'm going home to see Mick and Minn," Brynn told her. "Remember them?"

Someone called out from the hay barn, "Brynn! What's for supper tonight?"

Brynn looked across the barnyard and saw the ranch hands—Owen, Carlos and Jed—waving their hats to catch her attention.

She made a loudspeaker of her hands and called out the main dish, *fajitas*, which made them whistle and cheer loudly in anticipation. Matchmaker, looking intrigued by their rowdy exuberance, trotted over to the barn and immediately got three times the attention.

Smiling, Brynn got into the truck and drove away. City life, she reflected, rarely warmed her heart to the same extent that three cowboys and a tame deer could. Despite her move to San Francisco, she was still a country girl at heart, although not the naive dreamer she'd once been.

She was wise and wary now, *not* the dreamy-eyed softie she'd been before. Yet being at Wilder Butte was filling her mind with dreams. Which was unwise.

The distance to her parents' ranch was all downhill, a steep and curving descent into a pastured valley that lay just below the snow line. Once there, she found her parents and the dogs out in one of the sheltered sheep pens.

"I'm back," she announced, climbing one rung up on the pen's slatted wooden gate. "What's happening?"

Arch contentedly replied, "The usual. Feeding, watering, and shoveling sheepberries."

"Searching for more virus, too, and hoping not to find it," Maggie added as she moved among the placid woolly animals, examining them. "So far, we're in luck."

Brynn offered help, but her father put up a hand. "We've nearly finished. Keep your booties clean."

She leaned her forearms on top of the gate and rested her chin on her stacked hands. "Were my two little kitties good while I was gone?"

"Perfect houseguests," Arch assured her. "They've settled right in." His lined face creased in a teasing grin. "Were *you* good while you were gone?"

"Good enough that everybody ate what I cooked for lunch. No complaints—yet."

Her father pitchforked alfalfa hay into the sheep manger. "You went gallivanting to Bend with Flint, I hear."

"It wasn't a gadabout, only to do grocery shopping," she replied, thinking that he was somehow making it sound as if she'd spent a big day out on the town with her ex-husband. "Flint did his errands on his own."

Arch shrugged. "At least you're on speaking terms with each other."

Brynn reflected briefly on the extent to which she and Flint had spoken to each other thus far—the volatile arguments, the shaky truce, Flint's surprise declaration of interest, her own confession of wanting to believe him.

Her mother, peering into the ears of a bleating ewe, said, "It's good of Flint to loan you his truck, since our own is still in for repairs."

"If we had any snow at this level, you could drive the snowmobile back and forth," said Archer. "Maybe the next storm will drop more than rain and sleet down here. A big one's reported to blow in from the north day after tomorrow."

Brynn looked north and saw clear skies. Glancing back at her father, she saw his face undergo a startling change. An expression of sudden pain wrenched his rugged features. Almost as quickly as it happened, he turned away, leaning on the pitchfork.

Brynn gulped, seeing now what Maggie had meant. "Dad?"

"Huh?" he replied, sounding half-strangled.

"Are you okay?"

He gave a stiff, terse nod, without turning back around. "Fine. Just fine."

Maggie came to swift attention. "Archer, sit down on that hay bale right now!" She pushed through the sheep toward him, her face pale and alert.

Brynn started to unlatch the gate with fingers that trembled inside the wool mittens she was wearing.

"I said I'm okay," her father insisted, making an obvious effort to pivot on one heel and face his wife.

He looked pinched around the nostrils and Brynn could see a muscle twitch in his square, clenched jaw. She got the gate latch open, but a firm command from her father stopped her from entering the pen.

"Stay put. You, too, Maggie." He breathed deep, straightened up and resumed pitching hay into the manger.

Maggie halted in midstep. "Arch—"

"Just a hunger pang," he interrupted. "I should've tucked in more lunch than I did."

Brynn caught a beseeching glance for support from her mother. "Daddy, you can't fool both of us at the same time."

"You don't say," he muttered.

A mixture of fear and wifely impatience flashed in Maggie's hazel eyes. "Archer, please sit down for a minute at least. Catch your breath or I swear—"

"If you're going to cuss," he griped, grudgingly taking a seat on the hay bale, "I'll sit. But Brynn's got to stay out of this spat. One hysterical female badgering me is already one too many."

Brynn hovered in the gateway and interpreted another look from Maggie. It said to back off now that Archer was cooperating.

So Brynn relatched the gate. "I'm going in to see Mick and Minn," she said. "And I'll brew a pot of tea, if you'd like."

Maggie nodded. "Make it strong. We'll be there shortly."

Brynn left them and walked to the house, trying to calm her fears about her father's "hunger pang." He was too proud and stubborn to admit any weakness, and he'd been distrustful of medical doctors as long as Brynn could remember. Illogically, he had no such distrust of the local veterinarian who treated the flock. The sheep had a doctor; the shepherd did not. Her heart ached as she thought of the consequences he risked by going untested and untreated.

A world without Archer McBride in it was not a future she could envision. He had a long, happy life ahead of him if he'd only be reasonable and get medical help.

Brynn grimaced, shaking her head. Asking men— like her father and Flint—to be reasonable was futile. There was no manipulating them, either. They were what they were and compromise held no charm for them.

Entering the house through the kitchen door, she found her cats snoozing in a warm spot—on top of the fridge. Her parents had put a shearling wool cushion there for Mick and Minn's comfort.

"You're getting spoiled rotten," Brynn chided them affectionately. They came down, meowing and purring, into her arms. Not the children she wished she had, but next best to having babes of her own.

Held by magnets to the fridge door were recent snapshots of Laurel's two children, Krista and Jonathan, aged four and two. Both resembled their father, Cord Hayden, more than Laurel. Another photo showed the four of them together, all sharing a big bear hug in front of the Christmas tree.

Brynn studied the photos and wondered what impact the happy family picture had on Flint. He must have seen them this morning when he brought her home.

This morning . . . it seemed so long ago, as if several days had passed since her arrival. It gave her something of a shock to realize this was only the second day of her vacation, with twelve days still ahead. Strange, she hadn't crossed any time zones from San Francisco to central Oregon, but time did seem to have raced by in between. Only the day before yesterday she'd been staring aghast at six flopped soufflés, but it seemed to have taken place in the distant past.

And so much had happened today that she should be feeling at least a little worn-out. She'd gone jaw to jaw with Flint most of the morning, then cooked lunch for a crowd before noon. Yet she felt energized now, looking forward to cooking the *fajita* dinner tonight, and hoping to help Maggie prod Arch out of denial.

"It's time for tea," she told Mick and Minn, lowering them to the floor. They followed her around, sashaying against her legs as she boiled water and measured Darjeeling into her mother's Blue Willow teapot.

Arch and Maggie came in. He was still grumbling, acting offended and put upon. She looked anxious, concerned and at the end of her patience with him. They disappeared to wash up and change clothes.

Brynn had never in her life seen them so at odds. They'd had domestic spats before, of course, but had never stayed piqued for more than five minutes afterward. She was the child of parents who visibly loved each other, who smooched and cuddled night and day, who took a sleepless nap together almost every afternoon.

Maggie returned, saying in a low voice, "Laurel called today. I invited her to come visit while you're here, since the more of us there are to confront Arch, the better."

"A family intervention," Brynn surmised as she set a milk pitcher and sugar bowl on the table.

"Exactly. Laurel's not sure she can break away, though." Maggie frowned. "She sounded ... funny ... almost weary. I wish she could have visited at Christmas last month."

"It wouldn't have been fair," Brynn reminded her.

Laurel and Cord had an equitable arrangement of spending Christmas in odd years with one family, and in even years with the other. Each year left one or the other family missing them on that special holiday, though. And in Arch and Maggie's case, Cord wasn't one of their favorite people, although they hid it so completely that only Brynn knew how they felt.

She shared the same feeling and also hid it. The McBrides felt Cord was a flashy fast-talker who lacked substance and character. Laurel was blind to it, so Brynn and her parents pretended to have the same blind spot. They would never risk any estrangement with Laurel and the children, for Arch and Maggie were doting grandparents and Brynn loved being an aunt. All in all, the deception contributed to the family good.

Arch entered the kitchen and Maggie's tone changed from confidential to casual.

"Let's keep our fingers crossed that Laurel can break away soon with the kids for a visit while you're here."

"Amen," Arch agreed, looking unaware that a family conspiracy was in the making. "That tea smells good, Brynn." He gave Maggie a teasing wink. "Almost as good as when my better half makes it."

Brynn poured tea into their cups, relieved to see her father flirting with her mother again. Maggie tousled his hair in response. They were back to normal, but for how long?

Settling into a chair at the table with them, Brynn stirred the tea in her cup and switched from worrying about her father to worrying about her sister's possible visit. If Laurel came, what effect would it have on Flint? Would it cool—or stop—the warming trend Brynn had begun to experience with him?

"Earth to Brynn," she heard her mother saying. "Come in from outer space."

Brynn blinked. "Present and accounted for, Mom. It's good to be home."

Her father twinkled his eyes at her. "It's a treat to have you here."

They all settled into a comfortable conversation about the sheep, the price of wool, Brynn's job at the St. Martin.

Presently her father said, "This next storm might ice the road leading down from Wilder Butte. Think about keeping a change of clothes there in case of bad weather. You might have to stay overnight if the road is too dangerous to drive."

"I stayed overnight in the cook's room once last week," Maggie said. "Terrible black ice on Sundown Curve. The road crew didn't get it graveled until long after midnight."

Brynn could see the wisdom of what they were saying. Even Flint's Bronco wouldn't carry her safely over black ice on a curved, downhill grade.

She murmured, "I suppose I should be prepared, then."

But what really could prepare her for staying overnight at the home she'd once lived in as Flint's wife?

Her father glanced at the wall clock. "It's nearly time for you to head on up there."

"I'll be back before you know it," Brynn said, trying to sound lighthearted.

She packed a tote before leaving, and took it with her, but remained undecided about which was the greater risk—an icy road or the man she loved.

LIGHT WAS SHINING out the windows of Flint's saddle workshop when she reached Wilder Butte. She could see him tooling a piece of leather with Matchmaker watching over his shoulder. Roper could be seen there, too, smoking a cigarette and shooting the bull with Flint.

When Brynn reached the garage, she backed in, took up her overnight bag and entered the kitchen, where she found Constanza sorting out silverware.

Brynn told her, "I've brought some things in case I ever need to stay over in the cook's room."

Constanza nodded approvingly. "The next storm will be fierce. You will find the room ready for you."

Brynn took the bag there. Situated between the kitchen and Flint's office, the room was small, comfortable, furnished country-style, and equipped with its own bath and TV. It would do quite well overnight, during a storm. She could also use it as a retreat for brief breaks.

Setting her bag on the bed, she crossed the room to look out the window, which had a view of Flint's saddle shop. The lights were out now.

Hearing a step behind her, she turned and found Flint in the open doorway.

"There you are," he said. He came into the room and glanced questioningly at the tote on the bed. "Planning to stay anytime soon?"

"Only if bad weather ever forces me to," she replied.

He said, "Night after tomorrow it might."

"Well, if it does, I'm prepared."

He nodded. "How'd your day go after you left?"

"I had a nice visit with Mom and Dad. What about you?"

The room seemed to have grown smaller now that Flint had stepped in. Brynn could almost feel the power of his body vitalizing the atmosphere. The intimacy of being in a bedroom with him was almost too much.

"Me?" he replied with a shrug. "Same old."

Brynn saw that his dark hair was rumpled, and she resisted an urge to reach out and smooth back an unruly lock that sprang over his forehead. It took an even greater effort not to let her attention linger on his lips, or lock into his compelling blue gaze.

He moved closer and his scent came to her, a natural blend of saddle leather, pine and fresh air. So familiar from long ago. So very provocative at the moment.

"'Same old'?" she echoed conversationally, dropping her eyes, wanting to edge past him to the door and escape.

He explained, "Going it alone year after year is starting to get to me, I guess. It's not . . . enough."

Brynn watched him reach back and push the door closed. Then he moved closer still until he was standing less than two feet from her. He slid a finger under her chin.

"Look at me again," he urged. "Tell me you know what I mean."

She let him tip her face up slowly. "I've been lonely myself, much of the time. It had a lot to do with why I got married the second time."

Flint was surprised by her admission. And equally caught unaware by his own changing feelings toward her. They kept urging him to push a little further each time he got alone with Brynn.

He said, "When you left today, something went with you . . . something I seem to need. . . ."

Touching her soft skin and inhaling her subtle perfume was making him feel impulsive, reckless.

"Flint, you're confusing me."

"I'm confusing myself, too," he said softly, stepping forward and gathering her into his arms. "Waiting for you to make the next move is more than I can stand. If you don't want another kiss from me, you'd better say so now."

Feeling dizzy and weak-kneed, Brynn closed her eyes. "I don't know what to say. I—"

"Lift a kiss up here to me, Brynn. Give it half a chance this time."

Brynn wavered, then gave in, gave it more than half a chance. And caution slid away. Her lips met his, then parted in a headlong welcome she couldn't deny him any longer. Nor could she reject his exploring tongue and the raw, dark taste of his desire mingled with her own.

He brought one hand to her breast, over the woolen sweater she was wearing and caressed her with eager, kneading fingers. They centered on her nipple, drawing forth sensations she couldn't withstand.

He crushed her more tightly against his tall, solid body and she went willingly. She linked her arms around his neck and clung to him, invited his tongue more deeply into her mouth, risked too much.

Oh, dear God, she was sinking in over her head. His hand was under her sweater now, rubbing soft and rousing circles over the silky cup of her bra. He was shaking and she was shaking and she'd drown if she didn't surface soon and regain her breath, her good sense, her willpower. They would all be gone, swept away into the maelstrom of her love for him.

Gone, and nothing in return but the bitter taste of heartbreak.

Head reeling, she broke the kiss and gasped, "Flint— for heaven's sake—"

They stood, gripping each other, breathing hard, swaying on their feet. Flint's hand kept on moving under her sweater. He edged her bra cup down and filled his palm with her bared breast, stroking his thumb over the crest while gazing down into her eyes.

He murmured, "You give me a kiss like that and what do you expect? I want you more than I want to breathe."

"No." Brynn shook her head and made a supreme effort not to sigh with pleasure from the erotic motion of his thumb. "We're not going to do this."

"Brynn, you want this. I can feel every bit how much."

"I don't have the will to stop you," she admitted, arching into his caress. "But I'm telling *you* to stop."

"Tell me why."

"You don't love me."

He stopped then, gave a low, husky groan and slowly drew his hand out from beneath her sweater. "That's beside our point here. I mean, you're showing as much interest in me as I am in you."

Brynn struggled out of his tight embrace. "It's basic instinct," she said shakily. "Nothing more."

"Maybe so." He brought his hands to her shoulders and steadied her. "Or maybe not. For all we know, we could get more than sex going for us this time."

"Working backward from sex to love isn't my style, Flint."

"Even so," he countered, "if one thing keeps leading to another like this, we're both—"

Brynn cut him off by pushing past him to the door. "I've got to cook dinner."

He caught her back by the elbow with gruff impatience. "First, you've got to stop giving me mixed signals. You kiss me, you let me touch you, then you run. What am I supposed to make of that?"

"I didn't invite you in here," she snapped. "You invited yourself. And then you took advantage of the one thing we used to have in common—sexual attraction."

He retorted, "I asked first, then you gave what I asked for, Brynn. And more!"

"You shouldn't have asked in the first place!"

"That's the biggest crock I've ever heard. Once I asked, you shouldn't have answered yes!"

"My answer from now on is no, Flint, so keep your distance!"

Brynn jerked her arm out of his steely grip and left the cook's room. Returning to the kitchen, she tied on an apron and took several deep breaths to calm her temper and shore up her resolve.

She glanced into the great room where the two married couples were gathered by the fieldstone fireplace. One of the women was playing "I Will Always Love You" on the old upright piano.

My ever-lovin' theme song, Brynn thought with a bitter pang. She washed her hands, sharpened a chef's knife and started fixing dinner.

As she worked, she tried to put Flint's words and his actions out of her mind, but all together they resisted her best efforts. She didn't know whether to count on him keeping his distance or not. And she was as uncertain of his motives as she was of her own ability to resist him.

If, for some reason, he didn't back off . . . how long could she hold out?

9

BRYNN'S *FAJITAS* RECEIVED glowing compliments during and after dinner. Roper and the boys repaired to the bunkhouse after dessert, leaving Flint, the four guests and Matchmaker gathered by the fire in the great room. Brynn and Constanza joined forces to clean up the kitchen.

Constanza commented, "The guests we now have are very nice."

Brynn agreed. They were from Portland, two middle-aged couples, of which both women were music teachers and the men both in business. Pleasant and friendly, the Newtons and Lyells had come to relax in the rustic comfort of a working cattle ranch.

One of the ladies could be heard playing a soft, muted rendition of a romantic Elvis tune on the piano, "Can't Help Falling in Love."

Sweeping the floor, Constanza asked Brynn, "You are enjoying your work here?"

"Yes. Are you?"

"*Sí.* I love my work. Señor Flint is my best boss. But a lonely man, you know?"

Brynn hedged, "I hadn't really noticed."

"He takes notice of *you.*"

"Not in the way you think, Constanza."

"Have you not heard *amor con amor se paga?* Love is repaid with love."

To which Brynn wryly countered, "Have you not heard it takes two to tango?"

"Olé, the tango." Constanza sighed, making a dance partner of the broom. "That is my music, the song of romance. You are a romantic person, too?"

"Not after two divorces."

The piano music could be heard in the background. Poignant and evocative, it floated through the house, mingling with the sound of idle conversation from the great room.

Brynn could hear the deep timbre of Flint's voice among the others. Constanza had told her he usually spent a while playing host after dinner. Brynn thought it must be tiresome for him at times, maybe one aspect of the "same old" he'd referred to earlier.

Or maybe not. If he really was lonely, perhaps he welcomed the company provided by an ongoing variety of guests.

It would explain why he'd started renting out rooms after the divorce. Brynn knew it hadn't been his original plan when he purchased Wilder Butte; he had bought it to share with Laurel and raise a big family.

During the short time Brynn had been married to him, there had only been herself, Flint, the same three ranch hands, and a large herd of purebred cattle.

Things weren't as simple here now. And yet how familiar everything seemed all the same, even though the house had never truly become her home. Brynn bowed her head sadly and hung up her apron.

She said, "I'm finished until breakfast, Constanza. Thank you for your help."

The piano stopped, and she heard the sound of voices drifting out of the great room. "Good night," Flint was saying. "Good night."

Constanza cocked an ear in his direction. "I hear him coming to notice you."

Brynn also heard his bootsteps approaching, but silently disagreed with Constanza's opinion of his intent.

He pushed open the door and came into the kitchen. After praising them both for the dinner, he lingered, leaning against the counter. Brynn felt his eyes on her, intent and discomfiting.

"Do you wish for another dessert?" Constanza asked him. "More coffee?"

"No, thanks. You're both finished up already?"

"As you see, *señor*, we work hard for you."

"Yep. I sure do appreciate it, too."

Brynn went to the row of clothes hooks near the door where her parka and mittens were hung. "Good night, Constanza, Flint. See you at breakfast."

The maid, disappearing into the dining room with the broom, gave a little wave. *"Buenas noches."*

"Brynn," Flint said. "Don't go away mad, okay?" He crossed the kitchen to where she was putting on her parka.

She shrugged. "I've calmed down."

He was silent for a moment, then said, "You take care driving home. Especially driving over that icy spot on Sundown Curve."

She reminded him that it was well graveled and that she'd driven over it twice already today. "Don't worry, I won't wreck your truck."

"The Bronc's not my worry," he murmured, pushing off from the counter. "Just take that curve real slow, you hear?"

"No warning is needed, Flint." Sensing the real reason why he was overemphasizing the danger, she added, "Laurel was the reckless driver, not me."

"*If* that's who I was thinking of," he drawled defensively.

Brynn put on her parka. "I can never be sure." She accidentally dropped one of her mittens as she pulled on its mate.

Flint swiped it up from the floor. "You always think the worst of my motives, no matter what." He held on to the mitten.

Brynn put out her hand. "Can I have my mitten?"

He stuffed it into his right front jeans pocket. "Give me a break first. Kick around the newfangled idea that I don't have Laurel on the brain when I'm looking at you. What would it hurt you to do that much?"

"It would hurt to believe it and—" She stopped, biting her lip against a surge of sorrow and dammed-up tears.

Flint's tone softened. "And what? Find out it's not true?"

"It's a possibility, Flint. I'm not the gullible fool I used to be." Fighting to keep her emotions under control, she put out her hand again for him to return the mitten.

Flint didn't give it back. Instead, he took her hand in his. "You've changed a lot, you know. That's what's got me so almighty intrigued about you." He rubbed his thumb gently, persuasively over her palm.

Brynn knew she should pull her hand out of his, but she couldn't make herself reject the contact. It felt too good, even though it was jeopardizing her earlier warning for him to keep his distance.

"It's not just basic instinct," he went on. "And not anything to do with you looking like Laurel."

She bit her lip. "What makes you think so?"

"Well, I look at you and remember you've got two cats named after mice. I also remember you can tell good *Pinot* from bad *Noir* thanks to a smart-aleck twit named François. Does that sound like Laurel, or you?"

"Not Laurel," she replied.

He went on, "You've got white flannel pajamas and a green toothbrush. This morning you had on little bitty one-pearl earrings, but not now. I heard you humming today after lunch, and you keep wearing a perfume I've never smelled before." He raised an eyebrow and gave her hand a warm squeeze. "You or Laurel?"

"Me, again."

He took out the mitten and slipped it on her hand. "Be extra careful on the road, Brynn Ellin McBride."

"I will. Good night."

She left, believing for the first time that Flint had her identity straight in his mind. Finally. For whatever it was worth.

EARLY THE NEXT MORNING, Brynn was back at Wilder Butte baking Dutch pancakes and grilling sausages for breakfast. Flint had coffee made—his only culinary skill—before she arrived.

After the meal, he went out with Roper and the hands to feed cattle, the guests stayed in for a quiet morning of writing letters and reading, and Brynn drove home to visit more with her parents. She spent an enjoyable two hours helping her mother dye wool for a new weaving project Maggie was preparing. Brynn hadn't witnessed any more of her father's pains, and Maggie had no new instances to report.

Since his birthday was coming up next week, they talked about how and when to celebrate the occasion.

"Flint has a standing invitation to Arch's birthday," her mother informed her, then added, "I hope you two are getting along better than you were yesterday morning."

Brynn was noncommittal. "We're muddling along all right."

She hadn't been able to decide what was going on with Flint. She feared being hopeful, only to be crushed. At the same time, she was helplessly in love.

Nonetheless, her mood was good when she returned to Wilder Butte to prepare the noon meal—turkey pot-pies and rice-raisin pudding. Upon arriving, she learned that the single man from Portland had checked in.

"Señor Dustin Avery," Constanza informed her. "He is rich from investment banking. Very handsome, like Robert Redford."

When he appeared at the lunch table, Brynn found Constanza's description to be startlingly accurate. Tall, blond, handsome and somewhere in his mid-thirties, Dustin Avery had movie-star looks and a star-quality smile.

He personally stepped into the kitchen after lunch and gave his compliments to the chef. Then he went off with the others on a snowshoeing jaunt.

Brynn finished up and went home again. She helped her father in the sheep pens, had tea later with him and her mother, and then returned to Wilder Butte.

The dinner menu was Italian—minestrone, osso buco, amaretto ice cream.

"Señor Avery has his eyes on you," Constanza remarked in a low voice after dinner.

Brynn had noticed him giving her the eye whenever the swinging door gave him a view into the kitchen.

"He's not my type, Constanza. Perfectly nice, but my heart doesn't skip a beat. You know?"

"He does not know this," Constanza said with a nod. "I predict he will ask for a date with you."

A few moments later, Brynn saw Dustin Avery peer through the small diamond-shaped safety window of the swinging door. Constanza beckoned him to enter, which he did.

"You are in need of something, *señor?*"

"Yes, a few words with the lovely chef," he replied.

Constanza excused herself and returned to the dining room. Brynn gave him a polite smile. "I hope you enjoyed dinner, Mr. Avery."

"Superb," he assured her. "Call me Dustin, please. I'm stopping in to ask if you'd like to go to a western dance tomorrow night in Glenriver. With me and several others."

"Others?"

"My fellow guests. Constanza isn't interested, but Roper is. He's going to meet up with someone there. Anyway, we're all going down together, so if you'd like to join in . . . ?"

Brynn wondered if Dustin conducted investment negotiations with the same sincere, unassuming, unthreatening charm he was showing right then. His style was easygoing, friendly and casual—like the group date he was proposing.

He added, "It's apparently charity night, with the evening's proceeds going to homeless shelters."

A dedicated volunteer cook for a San Francisco shelter, Brynn couldn't help but be persuaded. She knew, more than most people did, how crucially important community support was toward helping the homeless.

How could she say no? Or even pass up the opportunity to put Flint out of her mind for a few hours tonight? Dustin didn't appear to have any overt romantic expectations, either, so why not go and have a good time?

"Count me in," she said.

"Great. We'll leave after dinner, as soon as you get done. My Range Rover will seat us all, so I'll drive. Oh, and dress western." He gave her a blinding smile and left.

Brynn hadn't brought any western duds for her vacation but decided she'd borrow from her mother's closet. In fact, maybe her parents would be interested in going and meeting up with her and the others.

Glenriver was a big resort lodge near the Mount Bachelor ski area, and only a half-hour drive from Wilder Butte. The resort often hosted community functions and events.

During the drive, she'd be able to get better acquainted with the other guests and Roper. All in all, the evening promised to be enjoyable.

Brynn didn't wonder whether Flint might join the dance crowd. She couldn't picture him enjoying himself at Glenriver, for Laurel had dumped him at a dance there the same night she met Cord Hayden for the first time. Flint wouldn't have any interest in going where he'd lost his fiancée to another man.

The moment she thought of Flint, he strode in looking mad as a bull seeing red. "Come to my office," he said. "I want to talk to you."

Brynn got the impression it wouldn't be a sit-down talk, and she was right. Once inside his office, he shut the door and faced her.

"Avery says you're going to that dance," he said through clenched teeth.

"Yes."

"With him?"

"And the others."

"He didn't waste any time smooth-talking you."

Brynn resented Flint's tone, manner and choice of words. "He simply asked," she corrected.

"Yeah, right. Whenever *I* simply ask you anything, what's your answer? *N. O.*"

"You didn't invite me to the dance, Flint."

He scoffed, "Why would I? You ordered me to keep my distance in no uncertain terms."

"You ignored my orders last night after dinner," she reminded him.

"Only because I had something important to say. You didn't fight me off then, you know. Besides, I'm not a saint. And ten to one Avery's not, either. The idea of you at Glenriver with him doesn't sit well with me."

She bristled. "Where I go and who I go with doesn't have to sit well with you. It's no business of yours."

"You're my ex, Brynn." His voice rose. "*My* business, not that city slicker's."

"I was never your business. Yes, I was married to you, but for all the wrong reasons."

"You're still related to me in a way. Why are you shooting me down with Avery?"

"Why are *you* acting as if I'm Laurel shooting you down with Cord Hayden?"

He fell silent, staring at her.

She instantly regretted the insensitive words she'd blurted out. "I'm sorry. I didn't mean that."

"Point taken," he said curtly. "I know what you meant and maybe you're right." Opening the door, he motioned her to leave.

"Flint—"

"Go on, Brynn. Have the time of your life tomorrow night."

She stepped out and he closed the door.

Brynn had no further words with Flint before she went home, nor any the next day. He showed up at the table for each meal and ate his fill, but came no nearer to the kitchen than that. She couldn't tell if he was simply keeping to himself, or if he'd lost the interest he'd been showing in her.

At any rate, she continued her routine, going home during the morning and afternoon break. That afternoon, at home, she mentioned the dance to her parents.

"I've decided to go with a group from the Butte. Maybe you'd like to join us there?"

Maggie's eyes brightened. "I don't see why not."

"Good idea," Arch said. "You can ride back home with us if you want. Who's in the group?"

Brynn named everyone and when she finished, Arch asked, "What about Flint?"

"Glenriver," Brynn said, which said it all.

"Not his favorite nightspot," Maggie said with a sigh.

They sat silently a moment, remembering. Brynn broke the silence.

"Dustin said to dress western."

"I've got enough for both of us," Maggie said.

Brynn spent the rest of the time going through closets and drawers with Maggie, ferreting out clothes and accessories for the dance.

She returned to Wilder Butte with a concho belt, a fringed suede vest, and lizard-skin boots, determined to dance all night and keep Flint off her mind.

If she could.

She cooked dinner, hurried through cleanup with Constanza and changed clothes in the cook's room. Then she joined Dustin and the others who were gathered around the fireplace in the great room. Flint, she noted, wasn't there, nor had she expected him to be.

A few minutes later, she and the others were seated in Dustin's Range Rover, rolling down the road.

The dance, held in Glenriver's Longhorn Saloon, drew a large, lively crowd of locals from the Bend area, and guests of the resort. Arch and Maggie were already there with friends when Brynn arrived. Roper met up with his rendezvous, a woman named June, and they all crowded onto the dance floor.

Brynn discovered immediately that Dustin was a superb dancer. It wasn't long before a woman cut in on her. Then someone cut Maggie away from Arch, and Brynn finished out the first dance with her father. She searched his face for signs of pain, but he looked well and was dancing without any apparent exertion.

"It's good to have your mother back at home full-time again," he said. "You're not getting much of a vacation, though."

"I prefer being busy, Dad. And home cooking is a refreshing change from hotel cuisine, too."

"Well, good. I like to see you enjoying yourself."

She rejoined fondly, "Which I am right now." For almost an hour, she reflected, she'd kept Flint pretty much out of mind.

As the dance tune ended, Dustin returned to her side. "Next dance, Brynn?"

She danced that one with him, and the next one with Roper, and then with Dustin again—a slow one, to a romantic melody. Accordingly, the lights dimmed.

Closing her eyes, she was tempted to pretend for a few moments that she was in Flint's arms, not Dustin's. And that the hand holding hers was Flint's. So much for keeping her thoughts free of him.

She opened her eyes as a tap came on Dustin's shoulder, and was astonished to see that Flint was cutting in. His expression was dark, troubled, brooding.

"Hey," Dustin said to him, "changed your mind all of a sudden?"

Flint gave a curt nod. "I got bored playing poker with the hands. Mind if I dance with my chef?"

"Go ahead. I'll try to get over it." He gallantly handed Brynn to Flint.

Nearly breathless with surprise, she was gathered into the arms she'd been pretending to have around her moments ago. In the first few seconds, Brynn made an effort to keep a comfortable distance from him, but he pulled her close and flattened his hands on the small of her back.

She had no place to put her own hands except behind his waist or atop his shoulders or pressed against his chest. Without too much thought, she placed them on his shoulders.

He was holding her so close that his tall, muscled body seemed to imprint itself along the entire length of hers. She could feel the pearl buttons on his western shirt, as well as the silver buckle of his belt, pressing into her skin. His breath was warm at her ear, stirring her hair, heating her neck.

"Having a good time?" he asked in a gritty undertone.

She replied, "Good enough."

"Before I cut in, you looked like you were in heaven."

Brynn felt a flush suffuse her face. "What brings you here, Flint?"

"The socially acceptable opportunity to do this." He moved his body in subtle suggestion against her. "So just relax and dance this one dance with me."

Unable to resist Flint's body moving against hers, Brynn let him hold her as close as he wanted. She let her eyelids droop and then close.

"That's it," he encouraged in a husky whisper. "Slow and sexy."

Brynn's every nerve was responding to his solid strength, his warm hands upon her back, his hard chest crushing her breasts. Her heartbeat pounded in her ears and set up an erotic pulse between her thighs. Her breasts ached and her nipples peaked and Flint kept one muscled thigh rubbing sensuously between her legs as he moved with her.

Sexy, she thought dizzily. There was no man sexier than Flint Wilder. There never had been anyone like him for her. Brynn drew a deep, almost shuddering breath. An instant later, Flint echoed it.

"Avery's not the man for you, Brynn," he murmured.

Brynn managed to pull away slightly and look up at him. "Who's saying he is?"

"You came here with him."

"I came with everyone, including Dustin."

"I don't like his style, Brynn. Before you know it, he'll have you believing his supersmooth line. He'll have you right where he wants you."

Brynn stiffened. "I'm not that easy or simple-minded."

"I didn't say you were. I'm only—"

Drawing farther back, she interrupted, "You only suggested that I can't make intelligent, discriminate decisions for myself."

"I'm giving you a piece of friendly advice," Flint growled low in his throat.

"You're out of line, Flint."

"So what else is new? And now that we're off on the wrong foot here, I don't want you telling me I've mistaken Avery for Cord tonight. No matter how similar this is to the night Laurel shot me down."

She retorted, "That night is the last thing on my mind."

"Yesterday, it was the first thing on your mind."

Brynn muttered vehemently, "'Wrong foot' is right." She made a deliberate misstep and trod hard on Flint's boots.

He swore under his breath.

At that moment, not an instant too soon for Brynn, the music ended. She pushed out of Flint's arms as the band struck up a fast tempo and suddenly Dustin was there, taking her hand, twirling her away.

For the next half hour, Flint stayed in the background, not dancing, just chatting with her parents and their friends or shooting dice at the bar.

Brynn saw him from a distance several times, staring across the crowd at her. Then he was gone, out the door.

Gone, but not forgotten.

10

BRYNN GOT READY EARLY the next morning for her
mother to drive her to Wilder Butte. Just before their
time to leave, the phone rang and Brynn answered it in
the TV room where she was watching the weather news
with Arch.

"Mornin', Brynn."

Flint's deep, husky voice startled her. "Oh. It's you."

"Missing my Bronco right about now?"

Brynn got her breath back. "Mom's running me up
in a few minutes."

"Last night you didn't say Avery wasn't taking you
home."

"You didn't ask how I was getting home."

"Look, you were his date, not mine. You went with
him, why didn't you leave with him?"

"If I'd been his date, I would have."

"Meaning you weren't."

"I believe I told you that last night."

"It looked like a date to my experienced eye."

"Is there a point to this call, Flint?"

He was silent a long moment. "I'm on my way down
to give you a ride. So hang fire." He hung up, just like
that.

Brynn plunked down the phone. "Of all the rude nerve. 'Hang fire' yourself, you egotistical, arrogant, thickheaded brute."

"Flint," Arch surmised.

"Who else but."

"You two seemed to be getting along at one point last night."

"Believe me, it was an optical illusion."

Maggie breezed in, curious. "Who called?"

Arch replied, "Our ex-son-in-law."

"About what?"

"My ride to work," Brynn fumed. "He's it now, whether I like it or not."

Maggie smiled. "Chivalry must not be as dead as people say. What's so maddening about that?"

"That's what I'd like to know," Arch said. "Flint's doing us—and you—a favor, Brynn." He turned back to the TV, which showed satellite photos of a storm front approaching the Oregon coast.

Brynn glared at the screen, forced to wait for a ride she hadn't requested from a man she didn't want to see. The *last* person she wanted to deal with this morning—or ever again, for that matter.

Within a few minutes, he arrived. Brynn met him at the door and immediately stepped out, circumventing any chitchat with him and her parents.

He opened the passenger door for her and she pointedly ignored the hand he offered to assist her into the truck. He settled into the driver's seat and headed the truck up the road.

"We've got some thick air to clear, Brynn."

"We've always got thick air between us," she replied coolly. "If it's not about one thing, it's something else."

He said, "Come hell or high water, I intend to hash it all out with you today. Somewhere private, where no amount of yelling and cussing will hit anybody's ears but ours. Does that idea suit you or not?"

"A showdown? I don't know. Where do you have in mind?"

"Haven't decided on the exact spot yet. Wherever it turns out to be, just agree you'll go there with me after your breakfast chores are done."

Brynn stared out the side window, engaged in a mental debate over the wisdom or folly of trying to re-solve any conflicts with Flint. Being all alone with him would be dangerous, unpredictable. And maybe un-controllable, as well.

Flint kept silent until they arrived at the ranch. He brought the truck to a stop near the house and then gave her a look.

"Well?"

"Fine, in the interest of clear air," she heard herself reply. Despite every thought to the contrary!

BRYNN CALLED HOME after breakfast and told her mother she wouldn't be home until afternoon, saying there was more to do before lunch than expected.

Flint came into the kitchen as she hung up the phone. "Ready to go?"

"I want to know where first."

"A one-horse, open-sleigh ride, from here up the butte trail and back."

Brynn blinked at his surprising decision.

"Unless you've got a better idea," he added laconically.

"No, I'll go." She put on her parka and mittens and followed him out to the stable, where he had a shiny green sleigh hitched to a dapple-gray horse.

Flint introduced her to the horse, Cruiser, then assisted her into the front seat of the sleigh. The back seat was piled high with furry, fleecy lap robes and, after getting in beside her, Flint brought one to the front for warmth during the ride.

He gave the reins a shake and the sleigh was off, gliding over the sun-glistened snow, leaving the house and barns and outbuildings behind. It ran smoothly upon a snowmobile track that paralleled the cross-country ski trail, then meandered up to the back side of the butte and beyond into the wilderness.

The sky was clear, the air crisp and pine scented. Cruiser lived up to his name by setting a casual, easy pace.

"He can do the sleigh route in his sleep," Flint remarked, "with or without a driver."

As proof, Flint looped the reins around the brake lever and raised his gloved hands over his head. Cruiser didn't even twitch an ear, just maintained a steady gait.

Flint lowered his arms, adjusted his Stetson on his head and settled back in the seat. "Now, for all the air we've got to clear."

"There's too much to know where to start," Brynn said, folding her own arms in front of her.

"Wherever you want, Brynn. Be my guest."

"Very well," she agreed testily. "Where do you get off phoning this morning and quizzing me about my social life?"

"I had to know, so I asked."

"Now you do. I hope you're satisfied."

"No, ma'am. The more I know, the more dissatisfied I am. Last night I was so jealous I couldn't see straight."

Brynn tightened her folded arms. "So rude, you mean."

"Jealous," he insisted. "And edgy about what you said in my office the other day. I was afraid you were right."

Brynn stared off to the side, away from Flint. "I'm afraid I was, too. Your behavior last night made it seem more than possible."

He said, "Whatever it's worth, I've thought it through and I can tell you I wasn't making any past-present connections between you and Laurel, or Avery and Cord."

"Yet you had nothing good to say about Dustin at the dance."

"Look, I like Avery man to man. Outside of his city-slick manners and smooth talk, he's a decent person, which Cord wasn't, in my opinion."

"I agree," Brynn said, feeling only a little less aggrieved.

Flint went on, "Cord didn't give a damn if a woman was spoken for, but Avery would respect a standing bond if he knew about it." He paused. "Did you mention to him that you're my ex-wife?"

"Of course not. It wasn't—and isn't—relevant."

"The hell it isn't."

"If you think he should know, tell him yourself, Flint."

"Maybe I will. What's your situation with him at this point?"

"Entirely casual, not that I owe you any answers."

"I think you do, Brynn, since it's not as if I don't have feelings for you. If I didn't care, I wouldn't pry."

"If you cared," she retorted, "we wouldn't be out here feuding."

"Dammit, we're out here because I've got a genuine, growing, passionate interest in you." His tone softened. "Not what I had before. Believe me, every time Avery touched you last night, it was like a kick to my gut. You don't know the rough time I had while I was there and after I got the hell out."

Brynn caught her breath, then turned to look at him and questioned quietly, "Genuine?"

He nodded. "It runs deeper every day. I swear.

"Flint . . ."

"What?"

She unfolded her arms and shook her head. "It's hard for me to really believe."

"It's true. Just give it a chance, will you?"

Brynn searched his eyes for self-deception and found only sincerity. It made her think he meant every word he'd spoken. Words that it thrilled her to hear. Words she never thought she'd hear from him.

"You're sure you're interested in me. Not . . . ?"

"You, not Laurel." He reached out and curved one arm around her shoulders. "You, Brynn Ellin McBride."

Brynn felt his gloved palm curl above her parka collar, around her nape. There was the magic, magnetic sensation of rawhide leather against her skin.

His hand slid higher and cupped the back of her head. "Come here, Brynn. Hang whatever else we've got to straighten out, I've got to kiss you right now or bust."

Brynn knew how much she needed his kiss. Too much to resist the glint of sunlight and passion in his blue eyes, or hold herself away from him. With a rush of a sigh, and a runaway heart, Brynn surrendered to herself and to Flint.

Flint cradled her head in both hands and brushed his lips lightly across hers, as if needing to savor the tender contact first before taking the plunge. Then tenderness gave way to intemperance and his mouth took true possession of hers.

Brynn gave him the deep taste his tongue sought, and he took all that she offered. Vital and hot, rhythmic and urgent, his kiss stunned her senses and emotions.

For endless minutes, their mouths fused and fed on mutual passion that led beyond sanity to madness. His hands slipped down to her back and drew her body against his, turned her until she wrapped her arms around him in the same way.

"I want you so much it's killing me," he whispered hoarsely against her lips. "You're all I've had on my mind night and day since you came back."

Brynn lolled her head back and let his mouth press hot, stinging kisses against her throat above the collar of her parka.

His hands were busy behind her back, pulling his gloves off and then he framed her face in his bare, warm palms and ravished her mouth once more. His Stetson tipped off onto the robes in back and Brynn shucked her mittens off so that her fingers were free to furrow in his thick, dark hair.

"I want you, too," she murmured when his lips left hers to nuzzle her ear. "I can't help it."

Flint lowered her parka zipper and slipped his hands inside, on her sweater, over her breasts. His thumbs brushed over her nipples again and again, making her feel that she would climax just from that if he kept up the erotic motion.

He whispered her name repeatedly, all the while kissing her mouth, cheeks and closed eyelids, at times darting his tongue in her ear. She found herself inciting him with low sounds from deep in her throat, and then with seductive movements of her hips.

Bringing one of her hands to his mouth, he kissed her palm and then slowly guided it down the front of his body.

"I need you, Brynn. Feel what you do to me."

When her hand passed his belt buckle, she discovered what he wanted her to know. Hard and hot, he moved boldly against her touch.

His breath hissed through his teeth. "We've got to make love."

"Yes."

"Not out here in the open, Brynn." He eased her away from him and took up Cruiser's reins in one hand. "Get a move on, boy."

Cruiser sped up and took the sleigh dashing over the snow, whizzing along the trail. Flint kept one arm around Brynn, holding her tight on a wild, exciting, romantic ride.

In no time at all, they came to a stout, snug-looking wood hut that had cross-pane windows on either side of its door and a stovepipe rising out of the shingle roof. There was a lean-to filled with firewood, and an outhouse a short distance away.

"Warming hut for ski tourers," Flint explained.

Cruiser halted close to the hut and Flint secured the reins. Taking Brynn up in his arms, he carried her to the door.

The latch needed only a flick of her fingers to release. It opened, showing a Do Not Disturb sign hung on the inner knob.

"For honeymooners," Flint said. "Constanza's bright idea."

Brynn switched the sign to the outside knob and received a long, deep kiss for the effort. Then Flint took her inside and set her on her feet in a cozy pine-paneled room that housed a potbellied wood stove, a wooden table with bench seating, a gas-cartridge hot plate and various emergency supplies. Gingham curtains framed the windows and a stack of plastic-covered foam sleeping cushions formed a soft spot.

In the middle of the room, Flint kissed Brynn again, then again, with increasing intensity, then dashed back out to the sleigh, where he draped one of the fleecy lap covers over Cruiser. The others he carried into the hut. While he lit a fire in the stove, Brynn quickly created a cozy bed from the cushions and sleigh blankets.

Fire started, Flint closed the stove door and reached into an inner pocket of his jacket. He took out two condom packets and set them within reach. Smiling, he said softly, "We're set."

Brynn took off her parka, trembling, her body aching with desire, her knees weak, and her heart bursting with love for Flint. He captured her mouth once more with his, then sank with her onto the soft bed she'd made. The stove fire was already warming the air, scenting it with pine and a faint aroma of wood smoke. Brynn melted into Flint's embrace, half submerged under the weight of his long, lean body and covers of warm fleece and wool. She could feel every searing inch of his erection branding her hip through her jeans. There was dampness down between her thighs signaling her own needs.

Flint's mouth mated to hers with tender ferocity and she shared in the sweet frenzy, surrendered to needs she had too long denied. She stripped him of his clothing while he stripped hers off at the same time. He held her naked against his bare body and ran eager, exploring hands all over her.

"Brynn, lover, how'd you get so all-fired gorgeous?" he marveled, as he gazed upon her face and then do the length of her body.

She tangled her fingertips in the dark thicket of hair on his chest and whispered back, "How did you get too devastatingly sexy for words?"

With his fingers, he shaped the fullness of her breasts and swirled her nipples to hard peaks. She moaned and he moaned in response, thrilled by the sensual sounds she uttered. Then he leaned down and suckled, right and left, back and forth with greedy, escalating hunger.

"Flint," she gasped, "it's . . . too much."

He stopped, rolling his tongue very lightly over the tip of one breast. "Too much good or bad?"

"Good." She sighed and curled one hand around his penis. "You make me impatient."

"Lover, you just let yourself run wild. Let the good take you wherever it goes."

He kept on and took Brynn even higher with only the sensation of his mouth at her breasts. She arched against his tongue, approaching a crest of pleasure. She blindly curved the palm of her other hand around the back of his head to intensify the pressure. She went where the good took her, to a throbbing climax.

Flint savored her satisfaction, holding her close, whispering what a wondrous, arousing surprise her orgasm was to him. "I didn't know it could happen that way."

"It's news to me, too," she replied, catching her breath.

He slipped one hand down her belly to the delta of thighs and drew in a sharp breath when his finger-
nd her heat. Forceful yet tender, he stroked

within her soft, slick folds and slowly slid one finger inside her.

"There's where I want to be," he whispered.

She caressed his shaft in explicit invitation and murmured, "Take me, Flint. Now."

"I'd like to wait some, Brynn, but I can't."

They both reached for protection at the same time, fumbled to open the packet and put the sheath on together with desperate, shaking fingers. Brynn wrapped her legs around him as he eased his hips between her thighs.

The tip of his erection probed her, rubbed stimulating circles over her swollen clitoris. "I'm going in," he groaned. "Oh, Brynn."

Brynn felt him filling her, penetrating as slowly as he could to draw out the exquisite sensation. Braced above her, he looked down into her face with deep emotion. Tears came to her eyes at being joined with him again.

"It's all different, isn't it?" he inquired brokenly as he began to move.

It was, Brynn thought, digging her fingers into his hips to make him sink deeper within her. More different than she had expected. She had the feeling that Flint cared for her at last, that the heartfelt emotion in his eyes was for her alone, that his mind and body both distinguished the past from the present.

"Yes, Flint. It's like never before."

She drew him in deeper, squeezing his hardness, ing the agony of pleasure it gave him, rocking under him, loving him.

He gasped her name with each penetrating thrust, drawing halfway out each time and then surging back in. Brynn clasped her legs tighter and bucked against him. There was no uncertainty, no doubt, no holding off.

His breath and hers came in spasms, wrung from them both by pleasure and need and an urgent, loving emotion they'd never shared before.

Brynn heaved under him, panting breathlessly, and then uttered a piercing cry of rapture as she came. Flint followed her with one last, fierce thrust and a long, low groan of release.

"Lord, Brynn," he murmured after the last shocks and explosions were spent. "Is anybody left alive?"

She sifted her fingers through his hair and sighed. "Not a soul."

Flint rolled to his side with her in his arms, his body still joined to hers. "Did you get everything you ever needed, lover?"

"Beyond everything." She smiled dreamily.

He nodded. "I don't want to pull out, ever." He stroked her back and her breasts. "I want you again, over and over."

"Mmm." Brynn fluttered her eyes closed. "I want you endlessly, too." *I love you*, she was thinking, *more than ever*.

"Brynn, look at me." He went silent until she did as asked. "What if I'm falling in love with you?"

caught a breath, then let it go slowly. "What if t?"

doubt me."

"Yes, and myself, too. We failed together before."

"Different time, Brynn, different situation all the way around." He cradled her against his chest. "I'm looking more to the future now."

"I'm not sure yet where to look," Brynn said.

"Think of how far we've come in these few days," he suggested softly. "In no time at all, I'm starting to think we've got something to build on."

Brynn felt joy leap in her heart. Still, she had to guard against repeating past mistakes, getting carried away by romantic notions, deluding herself with dreams that might prove impossible.

"It's no secret which of us loved the other when we got married, Flint."

"I was selfish," he said ruefully. "Too spoiled by success, too much in love with winning first place. Thinking back on that makes you afraid of history repeating itself."

"It could," she cautioned, "if we don't know ourselves well enough."

He placed a tender kiss on her lips. "I know I don't want to rein in what's happening to me with you. It's enough for me to go forward on, day by day. But without you, it goes nowhere."

"You're far more daring and impetuous than I am, Flint. You may be having just a wild fling that you' mistaking for something more serious."

"No, ma'am, I never had a fling like this. I antee you this isn't any flash-in-the-pan af

Brynn lay quietly with him, and hor her. Fragile and tentative, but hop

After a few tender kisses, Flint propped up on one elbow and gazed down at her face. "You're making my
day like you'd never believe."

"You're doing the same for mine," Brynn said with a
soft, contented sigh.

"Tell me everything I don't know about you, Brynn."

"Starting with what?"

"Anything at all. Your cats. Where did you get them?"

"At the city pound. They were kittens, from the same
litter. My apartment lease won't allow dogs, but cats
make the grade."

"How big is your apartment?"

Brynn described her two-bedroom walk-up and its
location on lower Nob Hill. Flint listened intently. He
asked about the St. Martin, and the homeless shelter
where she volunteered. Talking about the shelter, she
paused at one point to collect her thoughts.

Flint commented, "Your soft, kind heart is showing,
no matter how much you say you're a tougher cookie
than you used to be."

"I *am* tougher."

"Not toward people in need. You're not a me-first
human being, or else you wouldn't cook at the shelter.
Another example of your lack of selfishness is Dustin
Avery."

"How so?"

" lot of women would see him as a big, blond bank
       But not you, Brynn. You're here with me, not

       tly, Brynn said, "If a portion of his ac-
       helter, I wouldn't mind."

"That's what I mean. You put other people first a lot of the time. For instance, you cook for me mainly to help out Maggie and make sure Arch has her nearby. For another, you do kitchen chores that other cooks would unload on Constanza. You see her as a work partner, not someone to do your dirty work."

"You've paid attention to things *I* haven't noticed," Brynn said, pleased yet overwhelmed by his words.

"Brynn, I've even got a hunch you're not all that wild about city life."

"It's not home," she found herself admitting wistfully.

"Not like a ranch," he mused. "Cozy fireplace, animals everywhere you look, house full of happy people."

"Including you, Flint?" Now she was the curious one.

He replied, "Yes and no. The herd is a money-maker and my saddles bring top dollar. But money can't buy everything I want."

"Such as?"

"Wife, children—what really matters. Year after year passes by. I'm almost thirty years old, with not all that much to show for it."

"You've got something to show for it, Flint."

"Like what?"

"You provide employment for several people. And enjoyment for every guest."

He shrugged dismissively. "Enjoyment at a price. But, hey, it fills up some of the empty space." His hand squeezed her shoulder. "Having you here, filling up more of it, is an unexpected treat."

Brynn couldn't decide whether he meant that she filled up space as well as any guest, or that he preferred her to any of his guests so far. She remembered the six months when she had filled the role of looking just like Laurel.

Then she put them out of her mind. Today wasn't about anything that had gone on before. It was about . . . new beginnings, perhaps.

"Do you date anybody?" he asked. "Your mom never says."

"Not since Kelly. I don't make time for it now." She bit her lip, then asked in turn, "Do you?"

"Now and then, but I always hanker to go home alone before the date's half-over. Not today, though."

Brynn drew his head down to hers and kissed him, wishing the day would never end. Flint began making love to her again, and hope stirred ever more strongly in her heart.

Foolish though it might be, she didn't have the strength to stop it.

11

FLINT TROTTED CRUISER home in barely enough time for Brynn to start fixing lunch on schedule. When they entered the stable, he asked, "Would you please sleep here tonight instead of going home?"

"Tonight's storm will probably force me to if it blows in when the weather report predicted," she replied.

"That's not what I'm getting at, Brynn."

She gave him a teasing grin. "I'm rehearsing what I'm going to tell Mom and Dad about why I'm staying here tonight," she whispered in his ear, "with you."

"Stick around this afternoon, too," he urged. "Keep me company while I make a leather collar for Matchmaker."

Brynn couldn't think of anything she'd like more, besides sleeping with him tonight. "Wilder Butte is going to notice and talk, you know."

"I don't care who knows what we're up to," he said. "The way you're lit up right now, Constanza's going to figure it all out the minute you go into the house. Roper will do the same with me."

Brynn couldn't disagree. "Mom and Dad will guess, too. Probably tomorrow, since it's his birthday and the four of us will be together to celebrate."

"Look, we don't have to hide what we're both happy about. They'll be glad to know we've got a few of our differences straightened out." He gave her a sharp look. "Don't be thinking we haven't."

Brynn met his gaze. "It's happening so quickly, Flint."

"I never was a wait-around kind of guy. If that's what you want, Avery's a better bet."

She shook her head. "No thanks. Look, I've got to go in and start lunch."

"Do I have company to look forward to in the saddle shop?"

"Yes!" she exclaimed in mock exasperation.

Thrilled by his persistence, Brynn went to the kitchen and found that Flint was right about Constanza. The maid's candid eyes widened instantly.

"Two to tango," she concluded, a smile forming on her lips.

Brynn played it straight. "Nothing is certain. *¿Comprende?*"

"*Sí.*" Constanza signified that her lips were sealed on the subject, and then she got busy setting the table while Brynn phoned home.

"If you don't mind, Mom, I think I'll stick around here this afternoon and bake Dad's birthday cake...do a few other things I've been putting off."

"Good idea," Maggie said. "He won't see the cake in advance that way. Let's celebrate between lunch and dinner tomorrow, if Flint can come over then." Maggie paused. "About that storm tonight, Brynn. The weather report hasn't changed, so don't worry us sick by trying to drive home. Stay there and stay safe."

Brynn did her best to sound as though she was grumbling about parental advice. "Yes, Mom."

She hung up and went to work, thinking about Flint and anticipating the magic of his lovemaking all night long.

WITH A LIGHT STEP, and Brynn gentle on his mind, Flint went to his saddle workshop after lunch and started designing Matchmaker's collar. The workshop was compact, furnished with a slant desk for designing, and larger flat tables for cutting.

A few saddles in progress sat astride horseback-shaped barrels. There were bales and rolls and bolts of leather in a variety of colors—primarily browns, tans and blacks—all of them giving off the distinctive hide scent that Flint loved.

He credited leather-working with making him a better man than he'd been in his rodeo days. A craft he'd learned from his father, designing saddles and working leather required concentration, creativity, imagination and patience. Flint often reflected that this was the only area of his life in which patience came naturally to him.

And, as things had turned out, he was even better at crafting rodeo saddles than he'd been at riding rodeo.

Roper wandered in to hand-roll a cigarette, light it up and have a say. He drawled to Flint, "You forget to keep your hat on out there in the sleigh this morning?"

"No, why?"

"Then you must be blushing instead of sunburned."

"Get to your point, Rope."

"Don't necessarily have one to get to. Just making my own personal observation is all. Never seen you so pink, come to think of it."

"Well, you're seeing it now and you've probably got a good notion why."

Roper gave a slow, knowing grin and nodded. "It's real becoming to you, by the way."

"What do you really think about it?"

"I think everybody here'll eat high on the hog for a long time to come if it leads you into the state of holy matrimony."

"There's no telling where it will lead, Rope."

"Maybe not. Maybe so. Women sure do need special care and nurturing is all I know for sure. Plus, you've got an old knot to untangle in this case."

"Yep," Flint agreed. "Wish me luck."

"Flint, I've been doing you that favor in my mind ever since your fill-in cook came to work here. Some situations just look right from any distance, you know?"

"Is that the point you buzzed in here to make?"

Roper blew out a smoke ring. "My two cents' worth of good horse sense."

He looked up as Brynn entered the shop, and swept off his hat. "Looks like you two got the selfsame sunburn out there on the snow road."

Brynn looked from him to Flint, who said, "It only stands to reason."

"Back to work for me," Roper said, stubbing out his cigarette. "By the by, Brynn, that was a superfine lunch you served out today. Yesterday, Owen says, 'Brynn could take a pack saddle and make it taste like filet mignon.'"

"Thank you, Roper. And Owen, too."

As he left, he added, "Sure wish you didn't have to go back to Frisco. I'm not the only one at the wishing well about that, either. So long."

Flint chuckled, watching him go. "He's related to Constanza, but not by blood or marriage."

"This is quite a fishbowl we're in," Brynn said. "Heaven only knows what the guests will begin to think as time goes by."

Flint shrugged. "They can like it or leave. I know what Avery thinks, because I had a man-to-man with him out here while you were fixing lunch. Told him you decided to concentrate on me and he shook my hand about it. Wished us well."

"So much for any chances I might have had with a 'wait-around guy,'" Brynn teased. "Not that he was ever my type, nice as he is."

Flint showed her the design sketches for the collar. There were several, all featuring the doe's name, address and phone number, as well as thematic motifs of hearts, flowers and even a cupid with a bow and arrow.

"She hasn't wandered away so far," he said, "but I'd hate to lose her if she did. Amelia and Hank wouldn't ever forgive me, either."

Brynn mused, "It seems so long ago now that we adopted her."

Flint covered her hand with his. "I like the way you said 'we.'" He lifted her hand and kissed it. "It's a long time from now until tonight. How am I going to wait all that time?"

"Maybe I should go home," Brynn murmured. "You're making me impatient."

"I hope so. I've got to wonder now why I never put any window curtains in here. The whole damned world can look in."

Matchmaker appeared outside the window at that moment, and Brynn went to let her in. "You're getting a custom-made ID collar, girl," she told the deer.

Flint rejoined, "A little thank-you present, for bringing me and Brynn together. We're not sure how you did it, but here we are."

The little deer settled down on a cowhide rug next to Flint, and Brynn thought again that city life held no comparable charms to those she was enjoying at Flint's ranch.

Including the rancher, himself!

IT SEEMED TO FLINT that dinner that night would never come to an end. It was delicious—salmon croquettes, home fries and dilled zucchini, with huckleberry pie for dessert—but it was the longest damned meal of his life.

Just before dessert, the first blast of the storm swept in from the north, pelting the windows with a wild mix of rain, sleet and snow. Perfect night to slip under the covers with Brynn, Flint thought, if only the moment would hurry up and arrive.

Then, there was a lengthy wait while Brynn did all the necessary after-dinner chores. He passed the time by the great room fire with the guests and their piano music, but his ears were tuned to the kitchen.

Finally Brynn emerged to thank everyone again for all their praise of her cooking and then she retired to the cook's room.

Flint intended to wait a decent interval before bolting up from his armchair and announcing he couldn't keep his eyes open one more second. But Mrs. Lyell, one of Elvis's biggest fans, started playing "Love Me Tender" less than two minutes after Brynn withdrew and the melody sent him straight to his feet.

He said something inane about salmon being worse than a sleeping pill, bid everyone the shortest good-night he'd ever spoken and hotfooted it to the kitchen to say a quick *buenas noches* to Constanza as usual.

She was there, raiding the fridge, the spot where every one of her fad diets began and ended.

"Howdy, Constanza."

"Señor," she said, "you are learning to tango."

"No, headed to bed. Early."

She nodded. "Tango."

He wasn't going to argue with her nonsensical remark. Maybe she had a carbo overload, or the huckleberries had fermented in the pie she was snacking on.

"Well, *buenas noches*."

She beamed at him. *"Amor con amor se paga."*

Whatever that meant. He left her to her forbidden fruit pie, and circled around the long way through the house to the cook's room.

Where he found the door locked.

He tried to knock so Constanza wouldn't hear. Fat chance, since she never missed an intriguing sound, even if a gale was blowing outside. Hell, she knew what he was up to and he knew that she knew, but a romance deserved at least a little bit of privacy, he thought.

"Brynn?" he murmured, tapping lightly. He thought he heard the shower running, or was it just the storm whipping up outside? He couldn't remember if she took long showers or short ones.

He gave a light tap to the door again, then put his ear to it. Shower or storm? Shower, he decided, hopefully not long.

"Señor?"

Flint jerked around, caught in the act and embarrassed as hell. What could he say? "Howdy, again."

"In your own room," she informed him, "you will find what you seek."

"In my...? Oh."

She nodded, beaming at him, and then shooed him away. He went, blushing for the first time in years. And as soon as he reached his room, he did indeed find what he sought.

Brynn. In his bed. Lifting the covers for him to join her...

THE NEXT AFTERNOON, Brynn and Flint went to the McBride ranch together to celebrate Arch's birthday. They took the cake Brynn had made for the occasion, a low-cholesterol apple torte with vanilla frosting decorated with an archer motif.

The storm had dropped two feet of snow in the lower valleys below the usual snow line. Brynn had never seen such a deep snowfall at the sheep ranch. When she and Flint got there, they found her father and mother out zooming around the closest pasture on Arch's two-passenger snowmobile. Arch usually had to haul it to a higher elevation to have his fun.

Brynn and Flint leaned against the pasture fence to watch. They practiced trying not to look as if they'd made love half the night.

Within the first few minutes after going inside, however, Maggie and Arch started giving each other meaningful looks. Maggie opened a bottle of sparkling cider, lit candles on the cake and Arch made a big production of blowing them out to the tune of "The Birthday Song." Mick and Minn even added some musical meows as they watched from their cushion on the fridge.

While Arch was cutting the cake, the phone rang. Maggie answered it.

"Laurel! Your dad just blew out the candles. Yes, Brynn baked the cake."

Brynn glanced at Flint, who was staring at the bubbles in his cider as if they'd suddenly become the most riveting sight in the universe. He didn't look up or meet her eyes.

Maggie's voice rose with excitement. "You *are* coming to visit? Great, bringing your little monsters. Uh-huh. Sure, we can pick you and the kids up at the airport. Day after tomorrow. Perfect."

Brynn gave another glance at Flint and found him expressionless, now gazing blank eyed at his serving of birthday cake. Maggie put Arch on the phone and signaled Brynn to go pick up their bedroom extension. It became clear from the tone of Arch's voice that Laurel's kids were chiming in on the other end.

Heart-fallen, Brynn left the kitchen. She took up the receiver in her parents' bedroom and heard two-year-old Jonathan wishing his grandpa a "hat burp day," and then Krista, age four, correcting his pronunciation.

Laurel came back on the line saying, "Where's my look-alike?"

"Here," Brynn spoke up. "Hi."

Arch signed off to eat cake and Brynn sat down on the bed for a chat with her twin.

"Everybody's missing me, I hope," Laurel said. "It's been centuries since we were last together."

"A little more recent than that," Brynn teased her. "Christmas before last, actually."

Laurel chided, "Brynn, Brynn, you sound like a certified accountant, you're so literal. Lighten up, lady."

Brynn immediately understood what Maggie had meant a few days ago when she'd said Laurel sounded "funny... weary." Despite being hip and dramatic as usual, Laurel's words had a muted tone. But mothering two children of Jon and Krista's ages was sure to be exhausting at times, and Laurel also did part-time modeling for rodeo promotion videos and print advertising.

Brynn said, "We'll have fun playing catch-up. I'll be here several more days."

"Bored stiff, I'll bet, coming from the sin city of the West. What in the universe possessed you to go *home* for a vacation when you could be sipping mai tais on Maui for two weeks?"

"The same reason you're coming," Brynn said, surprised that Laurel would even ask. "Dad. I saw him have one of the pain attacks Mom's so worried about."

"Oh, well, sure that's the main reason I'm going to tear myself away from Boise," Laurel agreed in a low voice, "but it's not the only reason."

"What do you mean?"

"Cord and I are headed for the rocks, and I'm not talking geology. Don't spoil Dad's birthday by hissing even one word of this, though they're sure to wonder why Cord's not coming there with me."

Brynn reminded her that there had been a visit once before without Cord. "Given that, they shouldn't suspect anything."

"That was when my problems with Cord first started, Brynn. Before that visit."

Brynn was shocked, since it dated back to less than a year after Laurel had married Cord. There had been "problems" for more than five years? And now, apparently, more. Or of a more serious nature.

"Laurel, you never gave a sign."

"You bet your sweet bippee I didn't. Far be it from me to look like a loser. And then, I had the banal idea that having kids would fix everything, which it didn't, God love them. Anyway, I'll spell it all out to you in wretched, gruesome detail when I get there. Put Mom back on, would you, so I can give her my flight schedule."

"Sure, see you soon. Hold on."

Brynn got Maggie and then sat down at the table with Flint again. He was having an animated conversation with Arch about snowmobiles versus sleighs.

Too animated, Brynn thought, *mostly on Flint's part.* His tone seemed forced, his voice unnatural.

He finally looked at her and spoke to her when Arch got up to open a second bottle of cider. "Who died?" he asked. "Bad news from Boise?"

Brynn wasn't aware of looking depressed and dejected. She hadn't heard good news from her sister, but she was being careful not to give away Laurel's secret. Perhaps Flint was projecting his own bad feelings about Laurel's impending visit.

Arch poured more cider and made compliments about the cake. Maggie came back with Laurel's flight schedule and posted it with a magnet to the refrigerator door.

"What fun," she enthused. "We'll have grandkids underfoot again. Temper tantrums and the whole kit and kaboodle."

Brynn made herself eat her serving of cake. It tasted not surprisingly similar to cardboard. The carbonation had fizzed out of her cider, with just a few bubbles to be seen in the glass.

She was torn between relief and tears when the time came to return to Wilder Butte and start dinner. She'd have work to suppress her sorrows with, but the workplace was Flint's place.

In the Bronco on the way back, Flint said, "Your folks' house is going to be crowded with two kids and all. Maybe you should sleep nights at the Butte during that time."

Brynn noted that he'd used the word "all" instead of the name he could have used. "What about Laurel, Flint?"

"What about her, Brynn? You tell me."

Brynn saw a hint of uncertainty and indecision in his eyes. She wondered what he'd say if he knew Laurel and Cord were on the rocks. Sworn to secrecy, she couldn't breathe a word of it.

"I can tell you one thing," Brynn said. "I'm afraid she'll always be a wedge between us. You haven't seen her in all this time."

"I hadn't seen you, either, until you landed in Portland."

"Which makes my point," Brynn told him. "You don't know what your reaction to Laurel might be any more than you knew you'd react to me in the way you did."

"Hell, Brynn, who can predict a reaction to someone after that long? Did you predict how you've been with me the past few days?"

Brynn wasn't about to reveal the deep, abiding love that prompted her recent responses. "We always had an unusually strong sexual attraction. It may be that's why we've been losing our heads, going too far."

"It wasn't too far for me," he said. "Where it goes from now on is up to you."

"Laurel's visit could change everything, Flint."

"Only if you let it, Brynn."

She felt he wouldn't be half as confident of himself if he knew there were problems shaking Cord and Laurel's marriage. Whatever the trouble was, Laurel hadn't sounded optimistic; she had sounded ready to throw in the towel.

If it so happened that Laurel became free to marry again, who was to say Flint wouldn't want to revive his courtship?

BRYNN DECLINED to stay over that night and went home after dinner. Flint had expected she wouldn't stay over, not after the argument Laurel's call had prompted Brynn to pick with him.

He sat thinking by the fire late into the night, long after everyone in the house was asleep. Past doubts were cropping up, nagging him, causing him to reflect on his courtship of Laurel and the engagement she had broken.

From his present perspective, he wasn't sure whether he'd loved Laurel or been in deep infatuation with her. He knew he'd connected with her on a visual level at first. A love-at-first-sight sort of phenomenon.

He had seen her—a dynamic rodeo queen—and instantly gone gaga. Much later that day, he'd learned she had an identical twin who was her spitting image in form but not content.

Within a month, he had an engagement ring on Laurel's finger and money enough to retire from rodeo, buy Kingsley Butte and rename it for himself, and plans to put down roots with Laurel McBride. A gorgeous wife, three or four children, a herd of prize purebreds—he'd have life made in the shade.

Laurel. A little more brass than class. A little more hustle than bustle.

Would it appeal to him again? Did he know for absolutely, positively certain that he could turn his back on it in the snap of two fingers?

If he didn't know to the last degree, he was liable to hurt Brynn. If Laurel's appeal no longer held for him, what would convince Brynn of it? What would banish her lingering doubts?

Would he, himself, ever be as sure as he wanted Brynn to be? The possibility of hurting Brynn was a torturous thought. Laurel's timing, he reflected, couldn't be much worse.

Flint left the dying fire, took his troubling questions to bed and had a sleepness night.

12

AT DAWN THE NEXT MORNING, Flint made coffee and got out of the house before Brynn arrived to cook breakfast. He strapped on a pair of cross-country skis and set out over the fresh snow on the ski trail. Along the way, he came to the warming hut where he and Brynn had made love.

He didn't go in, but stayed at the turnoff to the hut, leaning on his ski poles and recalling the passion he'd experienced with Brynn in the rustic hideaway. Morning was breaking all around him, softly gilding light on the tops of the snowdrifts and setting off a tentative song now and again from winter birds in the majestic fir and cedar trees.

In the distance could be heard the droning sound of a snowmobile. Flint skied on toward the sound and, before long, met up with the vehicle, a familiar one that had two people aboard—Arch and Maggie McBride out for a sunrise ride.

Still celebrating Arch's birthday, Flint thought with a fond smile. He loved Arch and Maggie, and felt a familial relationship to them even though they were no longer his in-laws. They stopped and greeted him. Maggie wanted to use the outhouse at the hut, leaving Arch and Flint to shoot the breeze for a few minutes.

Arch said, "It was a comfort to see you and Brynn on civilized terms with each other last night. It put the icing on my birthday cake."

Flint shrugged. "The peace might not hold between us, I'm afraid."

"Laurel's call," Arch surmised.

"Yep, that and all the trouble from before."

"Flint, if you'd like some advice, I've got some about you and my twins."

"Maybe I need some." Flint nodded. "Shoot."

"Well, the way I see it, you and Laurel are a lot more alike—personality-wise—than Brynn and Laurel are. Laurel catches the spotlight and you're no stranger to being the main attraction, either. A spotlight is only so big, though, if you understand my meaning."

"I'm following along."

Arch went on, "In my book of life, that old saying about like must marry like isn't about personalities. It's about individual values fitting together between people."

"Okay," Flint said, seeing Maggie coming back. "I'll put that in my pipe and smoke it."

Arch started up the snowmobile and Maggie got on behind him. They roared back the way they'd come, waving goodbye. Flint watched them go, then continued skiing, thinking and turning over Arch's words in his mind.

BRYNN HAD BREAKFAST MADE and Constanza was serving it when Flint came in from skiing. Brynn immediately saw the etches of a sleepless night in his face and eyes as he passed through the kitchen to the dining table. Just as she had expected, he was turning inside out over Laurel.

"Mornin'," he said, pausing for a moment.

Brynn murmured the same thing, and then he moved on.

She listened as he joined the others to eat breakfast, and yes, heard a subdued tone in his voice. Hurt and more than annoyed by his moodiness, she scrubbed the fry grill with angry vigor. Throughout the time it took for everyone to eat and disperse, Brynn steamed in the kitchen, reviving every grievance she had ever held against Flint.

She recalled every time he had spoken Laurel's name in his sleep, every tense moment last night, his cryptic greeting this morning. What had ever made her think she could edge out her twin sister in his mind?

Her own mind picked him and herself apart. *Is Flint Wilder any better a man than he was when he married his true love's twin sister for his own selfish ends? Not the Flint Wilder I know. Is Brynn Ellin McBride still a sucker for a lost cause or what?*

Constanza's almost constant humming began to grate unmercifully on Brynn's overstrung nerves. Then Mrs. Newton got the revolting idea of sitting down at the piano and playing a medley of cheerful ditties.

Topping it all off, Flint came through the kitchen on the way to his office. His moody expression maddened her, so when she saw Matchmaker trail in behind him, her temper exploded.

"Flint," Brynn snapped, "you know the public health laws as well as I do. Animals are *not* allowed in commercial kitchens."

Flint snapped back, "She's just passing through. Who are you calling an animal, anyway? Matchmaker or the head of this house?"

Brynn shook a spatula at him. "Both of you are animals. It's hard enough to cook with a deer underfoot, and worse with you in the way."

"This is my goddamned kitchen, not yours, and I'll break any law I see fit!"

"You'll have the health department down on your head and don't think I won't report you!"

"Go to hell, Brynn!" Flint stomped to the back door.

"Gladly, Flint!" Brynn burst into tears and threw the spatula at a stack of pie tins that promptly upset and crashed to the floor. "Hell is a far better place than your goddamned kitchen!"

Flint jammed his hat on, led Matchmaker out and slammed the door. Brynn gave the nearest pie tin a swift, savage kick. She could see Flint through the window, through her tears, stomping into his saddle shop. She remembered him retreating there during the marriage, whenever she cried. He still couldn't deal with tears.

That hadn't changed, so how could anything else change? She hoped he'd ruin every square inch of leather he touched today! Lifting her apron to her face, she sobbed her aching heart out.

A few moments later, she heard the back door jerk open and the sound of Flint's bootsteps. She lowered the apron and blinked. His long stride cut through the scattered pie tins, scuffing them aside right and left on his way across the kitchen to her.

Brynn saw that his blue eyes were blazing and his big hands were clenched. He didn't slow or halt but kept coming and took hold of her shoulders, lifting her up to him and then kissing her sob-swollen lips.

She was shocked, stunned and suddenly responding to his raw, primal power. Parting her lips, she shared in a rough, ravening, consuming kiss that wouldn't stop, not even when he bent low and carried her up in his arms.

It kept on—a mesh of moving lips, a clash of teeth, a tangle of tongues—as Flint bore her through the back part of the house into the seclusion of his bedroom. He kicked the door shut behind him, strode to his bed and set her on her feet beside it.

Their kiss broke and they stood, embracing, staring into each other's eyes, exchanging wordless insults and truculent apologies, communicating a mute accord to sate passion with passion.

Flint's hands dropped away from her and opened his shirt buttons. Hers untied her apron. Silent, breathing hard, they both undressed at the same time, each watching the other.

Boots, shirts, belts, jeans, socks—their discarded clothing piled up on the floor until Brynn had only her panties and bra to remove, and Flint had only briefs left on.

"Stop right there," Flint said, his eyes glittering, focused on the pink, silky lace that cupped her breasts.

He reached his hands to her, framed them at the outer curves of the lace cups, fanned his thumbs over the centers.

"Don't stop right there," she said in a throaty whisper. She circled her fingertips through the dark hair on his broad chest and spiraled in on the small sharp points of his nipples.

He pressed forward into her touch and backed her against the edge of the bed until her knees folded and parted and she sank down to sit upon it. Pulling him closer, she wrapped her arms around his hips and brushed her lips over the soft cotton knit of his briefs where the tip of his penis stretched the fabric thin.

"Lover," he gasped, cradling her head in his palms. "Careful there."

She hugged him all the tighter and rubbed her cheek up and down his long, hard shaft, nuzzled the soft, heavy weight of his sac. Slowly she lowered the elastic waistband and bared him fully.

She loved what she saw, the silk and the steel, the bold thrust of power, the pulsing heat and the rip-roaring drive. She inhaled his musky scent and pushed the briefs lower, let them fall.

"You amaze me," she whispered, tracing his steel with her fingers, touching his silk with her lips, tasting him with long, loving strokes of her tongue.

His breath made an explosive rush through his teeth, his fingers slid down to her bra, unhooked the front, kneaded her nipples. Then he pulled away from her mouth and kneeled between her thighs, arching her forward and suckling her breasts, licking and gently biting the taut, rosy tips until she whimpered and held his head away with trembling hands.

"Impatient, Brynn?"

"Always." She whimpered again as he brought one hand against the inseam of her silk panties. "Always."

Gazing into her eyes, rubbing lightly over the fabric, he followed the curving line of her cleft. "There's where I want to be with you, again."

She was the loveliest woman, he thought, with her smoky gray eyes and curly blond hair and rosebud nipples. So aroused and arousing, with her tongue rimming her lips as his touch ignited more of her passion. So irresistible.

He kept his fingers moving and captured her mouth with his, sucking the tip of her soft tongue, stabbing the tip of his own against it and then making her lie down so he could peel her panties off and see her with no barrier.

She opened her thighs, inviting his touch and his kiss and she went wild under his mouth when he tasted her. And wilder still when he set to gently sucking her most vibrant flesh.

"Flint!"

A whispered shout, a demand, a command, a fair warning, a mating call, his name on her lips brought him rearing up with his breath shaking and his heart breaking loose with joy.

"I'll be there, lover," he promised. "Right there with you."

The condom took only a moment and then he had Brynn locked in his arms, lying under him, poised to take him where he wanted to be.

She looked up into his eyes and gave tender touches to his face and lips as he sank into her tight, hot sheath, filling her completely. "There's no one like you," she murmured. "No one but you."

Flint pulled back and thrust in again forcefully, possessively. Over and over he made a fervent claim to be within her and surrounded by her. "We fit, Brynn. We fit just right together."

She closed her eyes and held him, drawing him deeper, into the deepest rhythms of sensual pleasure, tightening around him, repeating his name like a mantra.

Bracing up on one elbow, he caressed her breasts, flattened his palm on her undulating belly and then shifted his fingers lower to stroke the swollen peak of her clitoris and make her pleasure flare into open flame.

Her eyes flew open, "Oh...that's...yes..." Her nails scored his back, her hips arched up with the first spasm, and he gave up control with a harsh, unraveling groan. He went with her, headlong into the rash, reckless, ecstatic explosion.

Drenched and limp in the euphoric aftermath, they spent long minutes twined together, sharing soft kisses and purring whispers. Contentment, profound and tender, stole over them.

Brynn lazed in Flint's relaxed embrace and placed her hand over his heart. "You came back, even though I was in tears," she murmured. "You never did that before."

"I knew I couldn't fix your tears before," he said. "My heart wasn't in the right place."

"You thought you could fix them today?"

Flint raised an eyebrow. "They look fixed to me."

Brynn couldn't argue with that, nor did she want any more open conflict. She wanted to cherish the idea—even if it might be mistaken—that Flint's heart was in the right place, beating for her, not Laurel.

ARCH AND MAGGIE BROUGHT Laurel and the children home from the airport the next day midway between lunch and dinner. Brynn had cookies and malteds ready for Krista and Jonathan. The house was a frenzy of hyper-hectic activity at first, but gradually settled down to controlled chaos.

Brynn wasn't surprised that she and Laurel had exactly th same hairstyle and favorite shade of lipstick. "Twins," they chorused together, "are like that."

Later, before leaving to cook dinner, Brynn found a few moments alone with Laurel. Maggie and Arch had the kids outside showing them the sheep and the snowmobile.

"Something is up on your horizon," Laurel said. "I'm getting vibes."

Brynn tried to minimize. "I'm cooking for Flint."

"What!" Laurel looked shocked. "Since when?"

"I thought Mom told you. The new cook Flint hired is still giving notice, so I'm filling in."

"First time I've heard even the skimpiest little word of it," Laurel said. "I wonder why? Or maybe I don't, since Mom never mentions Flint. I don't ask, either, for obvious reasons. Although, lately I've been wondering if I could get him back."

"'Get him back'? You're married, Laurel."

"Not for long now. God, it's been a soap opera you wouldn't believe—except you had a suds story of your own with Flint, so maybe you would believe mine." Laurel sighed heavily. "I warned you against marrying Flint, warned you that a man on the rebound is always bad news, but you wouldn't lend me an eardrum at the time."

"My heart had a deaf spot for Flint," Brynn murmured.

Laurel smiled sadly. "Like mine used to have for Cord."

Brynn studied Laurel's down-turned mouth and downbeat expression. She'd never seen her outgoing, dynamic, magnetic twin look diminished in any way until now.

"What happened, Laurel?"

"For ages I pretended I had a reasonably faithful husband. I mean, studs will be studs away from home turf, and Cord's business involves enough on-the-road travel that I don't expect him to keep a padlock on his piccolo."

Brynn strove to look blasé and worldly, but she felt discomfited about Laurel's philosophical attitude toward extramarital sex. It made Brynn mentally question the extent of Laurel's own faithfulness to Cord, but discretion kept her from voicing what she considered to be a rude inquiry.

"Nevertheless," Laurel continued, "I draw the line at him flaunting it under my nose. Especially with the dime-store cowgirls he meets around town. I'm going to be a laughingstock in Boise if he keeps it up."

"Have you and Cord gotten any counseling?"

Laurel grimaced. "Can you see Cord jive-talking circles around a marriage counselor? I can."

Brynn silently agreed that Cord was glib, to a major fault, and unrepentantly so. "Do you love him?"

"Who knows? He's a good father to the kids, and a superstar provider bringing in ten times the income Flint ever had." She gave a grim laugh. "Flint would get a good laugh if he knew the man I dumped him for cheats on me for cheap thrills. Some choice I made between glitz and fidelity, huh?"

"You don't deserve Cord's philandering, Laurel."

Laurel said, "I'm at the point where I'll divorce him and cut my losses if I run across the right man. One with a reasonable income, who'd be a good stepfather for the kids."

Brynn couldn't forget who had once been the right man for Laurel. Laurel had once been the right woman for that man, as well. If Cord hadn't entered the picture, the present conversation wouldn't be taking place.

"Maybe," Laurel mused, "Flint. I mean, I'd be insane to overlook him while I'm here. He's single, sexy, never had a cheating heart that I know of, and I used to be engaged to him."

All too true, Brynn thought. In that moment she made a wrenching decision not to bring up her current relationship with Flint. Laurel's return was the perfect test to determine where Flint stood, and whether Laurel would continue to be a divisive factor.

It shook Brynn to the core to think of Laurel going after him, but the outcome would prove once and for all who stood where, and why.

Laurel had an optimistic glint. "It'll take some ballsy, ultracolossal nerve, but zip ventured, zero gained. Flint Wilder, here I come!"

13

BRYNN WAS IN FLINT'S office with him the next morning
before breakfast, looking at a wholesale food catalog,
making some ordering decisions. The phone rang and
Flint answered.

"Howdy, Wilder Butte Ranch."

Brynn looked up at him and saw his face change. The
alteration was so swift and sudden that she was alarmed
into thinking the caller was Maggie, with bad news
about Arch.

Then Flint said, "Laurel. Long time is right."

Brynn dropped the catalog and got up from her chair,
despite Flint's hand motion for her to stay. She wasn't
going to sit there and watch "ultracolossal nerve" in
action, even though she'd consciously chosen to run the
risk of her life.

She went to the kitchen and started breakfast, trying
to take comfort in the morning routine, trying not to
think the worst, but fearing it. Fearing it a lot.

Constanza, folding table napkins, kept giving her
curious looks. Finally Constanza said, "You are ill?"

"Just a headache from a kink in my neck," Brynn
fibbed. She described how she'd slept on the couch at
home while Laurel and the kids took up the guest room.

"The children and your kitty-cats mix?" Constanza asked.

"Not very well, yet, I'm afraid."

Mick's and Minn's tails had gotten pulled one too many times since the Haydens arrived. Krista treated the kitties well, but Jonathan, in the throes of his terrible twos, did not.

Brynn held her breath as Flint entered the kitchen. "Laurel wants to come over for breakfast," he said. "Pretty much invited herself, matter of fact."

Constanza went to make another place at the table and Brynn wondered if the invitation had been as one-sided as Flint was making it sound. He stood looking at her uncertainly and then returned to his office.

Laurel, Brynn thought, wasn't wasting a minute of her visit. Brynn warned herself to be prepared for the worst. If Laurel was really ready to leave Cord and seek a more satisfactory relationship, she might not hesitate to be sexually available—to Flint.

At the speed Laurel was already going, she might have him in bed before dark. If he cooperated . . .

LAUREL ARRIVED FOR breakfast in a big way that captured everyone's undivided attention.

She zoomed up to Flint's ranch on her father's snowmobile. And since everyone was seated in the dining room for breakfast when she drove in, there was an audience gathered to witness it from the dining room windows.

Brynn watched from the kitchen window as Laurel raced the motor sled in several showy figure eights on the snow before she parked the vehicle and entered the house through the front door.

Then, of course, the twin factor became apparent and Brynn heard exclamations of confusion and surprise from the Newtons, Lyells and Dustin Avery, who hadn't known Brynn had a twin sister.

"Brynn," Laurel called from the dining room, "come out, and prove I'm not you."

Brynn forced a smile and went out to stand side by side with Laurel for proof. Laurel's eyes were sparkling, her cheeks pink from the cold, her blond curls tousled from her drive across the snow to Wilder Butte.

She looked exhilarated, vibrant and vivacious. In comparison, Brynn felt like a kitchen mouse.

Dustin Avery marveled, "Identical, for sure," as he glanced back and forth, comparing. There were similar fascinated comments from the Newtons and Lyells.

Roper said, "I'll be swizzled, a matched set."

Constanza made a sign of the cross as if beholding a miracle. Even the ranch hands—who'd known Laurel before—seemed struck with wonderment at being faced again with the double likeness. As for Flint, his face was expressionless, a mask.

"Our own parents can't tell who's who at times," Laurel said with an enigmatic grin.

The only good thing Brynn could see in the entire situation was the empty place next to Dustin, where Laurel would sit. It wasn't next to Flint, thank heaven. Perhaps Constanza was responsible for that feat of social engineering.

Dustin sprang to his feet to help Laurel off with her snow parka and pulled her chair out for her with a chivalrous flourish.

"My hero," Laurel said in a perfect parody of Mae West.

Brynn didn't take much heart that Laurel might find greater appeal in Dustin than in Flint, despite Dustin's appealing looks. Laurel had never gone for conservative business types before.

Fears rising and multiplying, Brynn returned to the kitchen. Constanza followed her in with a coffee carafe to be refilled.

"Señor Avery has big eyes once more."

Brynn nodded. "Until he notices Laurel's wedding ring."

"No ring is there," said Constanza.

Hearing that shook Brynn up all the more, since Laurel had been wearing her rings last night. Laurel was going for broke to get Flint; although not divorced or even separated, she was signaling her availability. Was Flint getting the signal?

Constanza filled the carafe, saying, "I will ask how is her husband. And also their two *niños*."

"Smart," Brynn said, smiling a little for the first time since Laurel's phone call to Flint. Constanza was a romantic, but obviously nobody's fool.

At that same moment, the phone rang. "I'll get it," Brynn told her. "You go ask nosy questions."

Picking up the wall phone, she said, "Wilder Butte Ranch."

"Brynn!" Maggie said in a frightened voice. "It's Arch, very bad. My doctor and an ambulance are on the way. Hurry home—now!"

Brynn's blood froze. "Coming." She hung up, ran to the dining room and told Laurel.

Everyone stopped and stared.

"My God," Laurel gasped. "No!"

The next instant, Flint was out of his chair, in charge. "Brynn, call 911."

"Mom did."

"Okay, the shortest way to Arch right now is the snowmobile. Less than a mile over snow, versus three on the road." He looked at Laurel. "Key?"

Laurel scooted her chair back and pointed a shaking finger outside at the snowmobile.

"Gas tank?" he inquired.

She replied, "Almost full."

Brynn ran back to the kitchen for her parka and purse, then sped outside behind Laurel and Flint. Flint mounted the snowmobile and, before Brynn could catch up to them, Laurel hopped on behind him. Barely a two-seater, the sled had no room for a third passenger.

"I've got to get to my kids," Laurel said.

Brynn got a man-in-the-middle look from Flint. She felt a touch on her elbow and found Roper a half step behind her.

"I'll get you there in my truck, Brynn."

Brynn turned away with him and rushed toward his pickup. Behind her, she heard the vroom of the snowmobile taking off with Flint and her sister aboard.

History was already repeating itself.

ARCH WAS SPRAWLED on the living room couch, coming to his senses when Brynn got home with Roper. Maggie, tearful and pale, hovered over him, brokenly explaining what happened.

"He had a clutching pain—just awful—in his chest. Then a dizzy spell—severe one—"

The children were upset and crying, hanging on to Laurel. Roper coaxed them to put on their parkas and go outside to watch him do rope tricks.

After what seemed like an eternity, Maggie's physician, Patricia Allen, arrived. By that time, Arch had recovered enough to argue against needing medical help.

"I'm coming back, Maggie," he protested, struggling to sit up. "It's only a touch of flu."

Brynn put a firm hand on his arm. "Dad, it's not the flu. Let the doctor help you."

"Arch," Flint urged, "listen to your womenfolk."

"You can't fool three smart women all at the same time," Laurel chimed in.

Arch started to put up another argument but was stopped by another wave of dizziness. Dr. Allen stepped in and proceeded to examine him.

An emergency ambulance pulled up outside and the medical techs came in. Dr. Allen gave Arch a stabilizing injection and gave the ambulance crew instructions for him to be transported to the nearest hospital in Bend and admitted for tests. He would be hospital-

ized overnight, at the very least, and possibly longer
depending on test results.

It was decided that Brynn and Maggie would follow
in the car and stay overnight in a motel near the hospital. Laurel would remain home with the children, of
course. One of Flint's ranch hands would do the sheep
chores.

Brynn's heart, already traumatized by Arch's emergency, took another blow when Laurel said to Flint, "If
someone at Wilder Butte can watch over the kids, I'll
be glad to cook while Brynn is gone."

"That would help," Flint replied. "Constanza isn't
much of a cook, but she loves kids."

Easy as pie, Laurel became the stand-in cook for the
stand-in cook.

Brynn quickly packed an overnight bag, unnerved
by Laurel's innate ability to work every angle of every
situation. Flint, on his part, apparently held no big
grudge against Laurel for jilting him, or if he did he hid
it very well.

When Brynn emerged with the bag, ready to go with
Maggie, Arch was being taken out of the house on a
stretcher. Watching the stretcher roll into the ambulance, Laurel started to cry, then to hyperventilate as
emotion overwhelmed her.

She reached out for comfort from Flint, who put an
arm around her to steady her. Weeping for her father,
Laurel wrapped her arms around her ex-fiancé. Krista
and Jon came running, upset by Mommy's tears, and
clung to Flint's long legs for security.

Driving out behind the ambulance with Maggie, Brynn had a last glimpse of Laurel, Flint and the kids grouped together like a family. Waving goodbye.

BRYNN SPENT THE REST of the day and visiting hours that night at the hospital with Maggie and Arch. During that time, he became completely conscious and coherent and began grousing about being imprisoned in a "goddamned hospital for nothing worse than a case of flu."

Brynn, Maggie and Dr. Allen together convinced him he'd had a near heart attack and that he needed observation overnight. The doctor reluctantly agreed that she'd release him to home bed rest the next morning if he continued to improve and feel well.

Driving to the motel after evening visiting hours were over, Maggie sighed with weary relief. "A near-coronary did for him what I hoped you, Laurel and I would accomplish with a confrontation."

Brynn nodded. "I'd vote for a confrontation over a coronary—near or not—any day."

"Now," Maggie said, "my big battle will be to make him behave like a heart patient. Maybe he'll be more manageable when he gets home." She crossed her fingers for luck.

Brynn crossed her own, too. "We can still have a confrontation, but what about modifying his diet and taking the medication Dr. Allen prescribed?"

"You bet we will, Brynn. If you ever get married again, find out first if the man trusts doctors."

"As if I'll ever get married again, Mom. Twice burned, three times shy."

Maggie gave her a sidelong glance. "From what I gathered the night of your dad's birthday, you and Flint seemed to be exploring new possibilities."

"If we were, Laurel put a stop to it today."

"She's fed up with Cord, I suspect," Maggie said.

Keeping mum for Laurel, Brynn tried to look surprised by Maggie's suspicion. "What makes you say that?"

"A mother's intuition combined with Cord's shortage of moral fiber. Laurel doesn't deserve Flint Wilder after what she did to him, but she has a right to someone better than Cord Hayden."

Brynn ventured, "She seems to be going after Flint."

Maggie glanced at her sharply. "What are you going to do about it, Brynn? Sit back and let her try—maybe even succeed?"

"It's up to Flint whether she succeeds," Brynn reasoned miserably, "not me."

"Honey, I'm going to tell you something, and I hope you won't take it the wrong way. You're too much of a lover, and not enough of a fighter. When it comes to love, turning the other cheek can be plain foolishness and I'd hate to see you do that in this case."

"Flint hasn't even said he loves me, Mom."

"You love *him*, Brynn. My mother's intuition talking again, but you do, don't you?"

Brynn sighed. "Yes. Fool that I am."

"Then fight for him."

"I'm fighting in my own way, Mom."

Maggie shook her head. "It wouldn't hurt you to act more and react less if you want a life with Flint."

Brynn said, "I took action when I first went after Flint and look where it got me."

"You took it at the worst possible time, Brynn, and out of weakness rather than strength. Right now you've got the best possible time in the palm of your hand. What are you going to do with it?"

"I'm not going to hustle and manipulate like Laurel does," Brynn said, shaking her head. "It's just not in me to do that."

"I agree, but what's in you needs to rise to this occasion. You keep that in mind over these next few days."

Brynn made a face. "Yes, Mom. And I'll do all my homework after school and eat my cruciferous vegetables, too."

"You just wait until you're a mother," Maggie admonished with a chuckle. "Dispensing advice comes with the territory."

AT NOON THE NEXT DAY, Arch still felt fine and Dr. Allen released him with strict instructions about proper diet, aerobic exercise and prescription medication.

In addition to Arch coming out of the hospital, their other car was ready to come out of the repair shop in Bend, so Brynn drove it home while her parents drove the other one.

Driving behind them, Brynn could see his mouth moving and his hands gesturing. She could tell he was grumbling and griping about the medical establishment, the hospital stay, the food, the bill, the visiting hours and probably the ambulance.

Nevertheless, she speculated, it might be mostly bluster. He had seen below the tip of the iceberg now. It still froze Brynn's blood when she thought of how close his attack could have come to sinking him.

Arriving home, they found only Mick, Minn, the dogs and the sheep there to greet them. Laurel and the kids were up at Wilder Butte, standing in for the stand-in cook. Brynn wasn't clear on who had provided Laurel with transportation back and forth. She only knew that Laurel had called Arch at the hospital yesterday and last night from Flint's ranch.

Within five minutes of Brynn's return, the transportation question was answered as Laurel came driving in with the kids in Flint's Bronco.

They trooped into the house, Laurel looking bright eyed and upbeat. Krista said, "Guess what we did, Aunt Brynn?"

Brynn swung her playfully around in a circle. "I can't guess. What?"

"Went on a sleigh ride. Mommy, too."

Brynn's heart almost shriveled up and died.

"Hut!" Jonathan exclaimed excitedly. "Hut!"

She faked an auntlike smile. "Ah, you saw the warming hut."

Krista wrinkled her nose, "I went potty in a out-house."

They were so innocent, and it was so heartbreaking. Brynn braced herself to ask a necessary question, no matter how painful the answer would be.

"Who drove the horsie?"

"Uncle Roper."

Brynn brightened. Maybe not so heartbreaking. Maybe there was hope yet. A slim chance. Something to go on.

"Mommy cooked," Jonathan informed her.

"Did I ever," Laurel rejoined, returning from greeting Arch in the bedroom where he was following the doctor's bed rest orders.

"So the cooking went all right," Brynn observed.

Laurel replied, "Nobody's died of food poisoning yet. I had a fairly decent time slinging the hash. Wilder Butte wouldn't be such a ho-hum place to live."

Brynn could think of far more glowing assessments than the one Laurel had just given. "Well, thanks for filling in."

"It was worth it to get back on Flint's good side," Laurel said in a low voice. "I'm making inroads, definite progress."

Brynn's bit of inner brightness dimmed. "Such as?" she inquired.

"I'm going to take him snowmobiling tomorrow. Just the two of us if I finesse it right by making him jealous of Dustin. And I've decided to cook dinner tonight, without the kids there to worry about. You've hardly spent any time with them, so have a night off and great fun here being Auntie Brynn. My special treat to you."

Brynn dredged up a thankful smile, unable to be crass and say she'd rather cook for Flint.

So it was that Laurel cooked dinner with no kids to worry about, and didn't come home until two o'clock the next morning.

14

WITH A HEAVY HEART, Brynn drove to Wilder Butte in the morning to cook breakfast. Coffee was made and Roper was in the kitchen when she arrived.

He doffed his hat and toasted his coffee mug to her. "Welcome back, stranger. Glad to see your good mornin' smile again. Your dad's doing lots better, I hear."

"We're keeping our fingers crossed," Brynn told him. "Things went pretty well while I was gone?"

"You could say that, I reckon." Roper pursed his lips and shrugged. "Then again, you could say they're a mighty lot tastier when you're here."

Brynn could have hugged him. She gave him her most delighted good-morning smile. "It's great to be appreciated, 'Uncle' Roper. How bad was it?"

"The Newtons and Lyells threatened to check out. Flint calmed them down saying you'd be back for sure. Avery's still here, but that's to be expected maybe, since he's got eyes for your sister. The upshot is Laurel doesn't take after you and Mrs. Mags in the kitchen, and that's a fact."

He settled his hat back on his head and moseyed out with his coffee. Brynn was glad for that much to feel good about. It might be the most she could hope for from now on.

Constanza came in and made a big, happy to-do about Brynn's return.

Brynn told her, "I heard from Roper my stand-in wasn't so hot."

"Many pots to wash," Constanza confirmed, making copious scrubbing motions. "Many indigestions."

"It's a new day," said Brynn, "we're back on track for breakfast." She took a deep breath. "Is Flint around?"

Constanza hiked a thumb in the direction of the saddle shop. "He wears a bad mood." Then she whispered, "Señor Avery and Laurel went dancing last night."

Brynn deduced that Laurel's plan to make Flint jealous was definitely progressing if Flint was holed up in the saddle shop, his refuge, so early in the day.

He came inside just before breakfast, passed through the kitchen, bidding her only a brief good-morning, and sat down to eat. Then, back he went to the saddle shop, looking preoccupied and out of sorts.

Brynn felt snubbed and stung. It got worse, a little later, when Laurel dropped by in his Bronco—without the kids—and spent just long enough with him in the saddle shop for Brynn to suspect the worst.

However, Laurel then left the Bronco at the ranch and rode home with Brynn in the family car. During the drive down, Laurel said, "If everything keeps falling into place, I'm going to divorce Cord. It's really lucky that Dustin is here."

"It doesn't seem fair to make Flint jealous by using Dustin," Brynn said, her heart aching. "He's a nice man."

Laurel said, "He seemed to think Flint had a thing for you."

"Really?"

Laurel shrugged. "I'm going to make my major move on Flint today after lunch. He's going out with the Newtons and Dustin on a ski tour and I'm going to tootle by on Dad's snowmobile. Sort of kidnap Flint, you know? And then whisk him away to one of those warming huts up there on the butte."

Brynn was relieved to reach home, where playing children's games with Krista and Jon kept her from crying her heart out.

IN THE SADDLE SHOP after Laurel dropped off the keys to the Bronco, Flint set to finishing Matchmaker's collar and doing some deep thinking. Over the past couple days he'd had more than one occasion to relate to both Brynn and Laurel separately and together. It had given him a perspective he'd never had before on the two sisters. And he'd had to set himself apart from Brynn in order to get it.

No two ways about it, the twins were nothing like each other except for being look-alikes. Laurel had a standout persona, a shining-star glitter.

And Brynn had a shine of her own, a lot quieter, more subtle, like a steady candle flame. Compared to Laurel, Brynn had the more caring nature. If a man wanted to be cared for, Brynn was his choice. Compared to Brynn, Laurel was ten times more outgoing and social. If a man wanted a party girl, Laurel fit the bill.

Laurel wasn't a wait-around woman. Obviously unhappy in her marriage, she wasn't biding the time to get a separation or a divorce before checking out the prospects. Brynn, on the other hand, would never be on with the new before she let off with the old.

Laurel knew how to wangle an opportunity. If a man wanted an aggressive woman, vote for Laurel. Brynn knew how to wangle good food into great meals. Dinner to die for, vote Brynn. Hustle and pizzazz, Laurel. Stable and mature, Brynn.

Yep, he had a new perspective now on Brynn and Laurel, and it was getting clearer by the minute.

FLINT CAME INTO the kitchen when Brynn was finishing up the last of the after-lunch chores.

"How's about you coming on the ski tour today?" he asked her.

His question featured more words than he'd spoken to her all day, she thought. It also sounded like a consolation prize to the first runner-up.

"I'm glad you asked," she replied. "It saves me from having to invite myself along."

"Does that mean yes?"

"I heard about the tour earlier today and brought my equipment with me. So, yes."

Since earlier that day, Brynn had taken Maggie's advice to heart, and concluded that the passive approach was destroying her own self-esteem. Rather than watching and waiting, she'd be active and determined from now on. She'd mount an offensive against Laurel.

She'll have to get past me, Brynn was now thinking, *if she really wants him.*

"Good, then," he said. "Meet us at the trailhead in thirty minutes."

FORTY MINUTES LATER, Brynn was gliding and poling on the ski track behind Flint, the Newtons and Dustin. In the next half hour they climbed steadily in elevation through stands of pines and firs to the snowbound backcountry wilderness of Wilder Butte.

Presently, as Brynn was expecting, there was the sound of an engine in the distance. It came closer and Laurel sped into view on the snowmobile. A dynamic, compelling figure on the sleek, careening sled, she came to them and stopped, idling the motor.

"Mind if I tag along?" she asked Flint.

He replied, "It's a free country all around."

"If anybody gets tired or has a muscle cramp," she said to him, "I can give them a lift. How are *your* muscles feeling?"

"No complaints yet."

She gave him a flirtatious smile and purred, "Let me know if any arise."

Dustin expressed some roguish indignation. "What about *my* muscles?"

"Superb," Laurel pronounced, reaching out and giving his biceps a suggestive squeeze. Then she revved the motor to a slow speed and started gliding in lazy curves and circles, at times paralleling the ski trail, at times leading the way.

Brynn sidestepped out of the track where she was last in line and passed the others to ski abreast with Flint.

"So much for the grand silence of nature," she commented dryly.

"Yep. Love to suck in those exhaust fumes instead of fresh air."

"Do you care to explain why you haven't spoken more than a dozen words to me today, Flint?"

"I've had some thinking to do, Brynn. Can't talk and think at the same time."

"Thinking in what sense?"

"About you and Laurel. I was married to one of you and engaged to the other, which is overloading my circuits with both of you in my backyard now."

"Do you find it confusing?"

"Brynn, if you weren't a twin, how do you think you'd find it?"

She tried to picture two Flints on the ski trail with her and had some success envisioning it. If something fatal happened to him, would she be blind to his clone if he had one?

"I think I'd want to be very sure of myself if I were you," she finally replied.

He nodded. "That's what the thinking time was for."

Brynn saw his eyes following Laurel, and why wouldn't they? she thought. On the snowmobile, Laurel had the dash, the speed, the high visibility, the command she wanted of Flint's attention. Off the snowmobile, Laurel was no less of an attention getter.

Frustrated by the task of routing her sister from Flint's mind, Brynn fell back from the group to last place once more. She lagged behind, staring down at the ski track in a struggle with herself to overcome insecurity, eroding confidence, helpless love.

She heard Flint yell something at Laurel. Looking up, to the right, Brynn saw an avalanche area sign and Laurel approaching the area.

"Laurel!" Flint shouted. "Back off!"

Laurel waved a playful, dismissing hand at him and progressed farther into the snow bowl, gaining speed, guiding the sled in zigzags across the pristine, sun-sparkled snow.

Brynn's heart clutched as Laurel continued closer to the danger sign, still waving off Flint's shouts. Showboating, she went high up the slope and set off a minuscule snowslide.

To Brynn's horror, the tiny slide gathered speed and volume and segued into a down-rushing wave.

Heading straight toward Brynn!

She saw the sled catch on the wave's curling edge, saw Laurel desperately strive to ride the curl with the snowmobile without success. She watched in shock as the snow engulfed her sister.

Flint and the others were safely above the fall line. If Brynn hadn't lagged, she'd be there, too. Now Laurel, the sled and the tidal wave were catapulting down upon her.

Brynn screamed. The slide tumbled, snatched, rolled over and consumed her. She was encased in freezing whiteness.

Her breath crushed out of her. Darkness closed in on her. Muffled shouts and voices echoed above. Consciousness faded . . . dimmed . . .

Buried. Buried alive.

She heard more voices, louder, fainter, then jubilant shouts. Hands pierced through to her, grasped and pulled her up, up to the sight of Flint's burning blue eyes.

He was gasping, "Thank God, thank God."

Brynn saw Laurel, Dustin and the Newtons crowded around her. Laurel was caked all over with snow, tears streaming down her face, sobbing, "Brynn, I'm so sorry. My fault, all mine."

"Okay," Flint said, breathing heavily. "Everybody's in one piece." He stood up. "I'll get the snowmobile so we can take Brynn back."

Brynn turned her head and saw the sled a distance away, two-thirds of it jutting out of a mound of snow and boulders. Flint skied toward it, and as he approached, the base of the mound shifted from the weight of the sled. The shift kicked a boulder loose.

Brynn cried, "No! No!"

It caught Flint on one shoulder and the side of his head, knocking him flat.

Unmoving.

FLINT WOKE IN DARKNESS, head pounding and back muscles throbbing with pain. He felt someone's hand holding his, a pillow under his head, a cover on his body.

Memory came rushing back, reassuring him that he was alive, that the avalanche had happened three days ago. It was still fresh in his mind—the tidal wave of snow, the loose boulder, a period of half consciousness.

Flint recalled Dustin Avery getting him down the mountain on the snowmobile. There'd been a doctor after that, three days ago, saying, "Blow to the skull, possible wrenched back. Can you hear my voice, Mr. Wilder?"

Flint remembered replying, "Yep, I hear it. I just can't see you or anything else."

Not one damn thing.

And now, as Flint woke to full awareness, there was a grim knowledge reasserting itself—he'd been seeing nothing but darkness every day since the accident.

Each day, the doctor had come to the ranch, done an exam, said the same thing: "Your back injury should heal within a week or so. Stay in bed. The blindness from the head trauma . . . well, it may be temporary or permanent. Only time will tell."

Time. Day after day after day and nothing in sight.

Flint stirred, felt the hand holding his move, and murmured, "Who's there?"

"Brynn."

Somehow he had known that before asking. How had he known that?

"Are you feeling any better?" she asked.

"Hell, no." *Somebody turn on the lights in here, for God's sake!* He didn't have to ask what time it was, for he could smell it. Coffee, toast, some kind of eggs.

She said, "You'll feel better after you wash your face, brush your teeth and drink your coffee."

He felt her placing a warm, wet cloth in his hand, and he swiped it over his face. Then she gave him a toothbrush with a dab of toothpaste on the bristles. He scrubbed it over his teeth.

"We've got to stop meeting this way," he growled at her.

"Be nice," she admonished. "You've got someone here to see you besides me." She took his hand and placed it on something furry. Matchmaker's head.

Well, who couldn't crack a smile about that? So he did. "Howdy, sweet thing." He pictured the doe eyes and eyelashes, stroked the long ears.

Brynn chuckled and put a hot mug in his other hand. Coffee. Then she set a bed tray on the mattress next to him. "*Bon appétit.*"

He sighed. "Thanks, Brynn. A lot." He ran his fingertips over the tray and its contents, getting the lay of the land there. He couldn't see, but he could still eat.

Brynn, Laurel and Constanza were his nurses now. Laurel had extended her visit to help care for him—and atone for causing the accident. She brought her kids over at some point each day to brighten it for him.

"Anything else I can get or do for you?" Brynn asked.

He shook his head gingerly, because of the pain. "Not for a while."

She touched his hand again and left. When he was sure she was gone, he pressed his hands over his eyes and prayed to almighty heaven for his sight to come back.

THAT AFTERNOON, Brynn stood in Flint's bedroom doorway, watching Laurel plump his pillows. Krista and Jonathan were sprawled on his big bed, and Krista was telling a story.

He looked cheered, she thought. His sightless eyes followed Laurel's movements around his bed as she straightened his nightstand. He reached out, finding Jonathan's head and tousling the little boy's hair.

Brynn saw herself losing Flint to Laurel. In Laurel and the children, he had what he so wanted—a family. Biting back tears, Brynn returned to the kitchen. She found Dustin there, chatting with Constanza about the maid's birthplace in Mexico.

He smiled at Brynn. "How's it going?"

"After surviving an avalanche, every day of life is a good one," she told him.

He nodded. "You were buried pretty deep. Flint was a wild man digging you out, issuing orders right and left at the same time. 'Do this, do that, Avery, you save Laurel, I'll save Brynn.'" Dustin shook his head admiringly. "Cool head to have in a crisis."

Brynn caught her breath. "*Flint* saved me?" *Instead of saving Laurel first?* she thought.

"Single-handedly," Dustin replied. "He headed straight for where he'd spotted you last and attacked the snow like a snowblower. Newton and I had it easier with Laurel, since she wasn't in that deep."

Brynn was disbelieving. "Flint must have mistaken me for her."

"Not a chance of that," Dustin replied. "It was your name he kept yelling."

Brynn had only heard muffled, unidentifiable shouts. Now, hearing the details from Dustin, she felt her heart fill with happiness and hope.

She excused herself, left the kitchen and returned to Flint's bedroom doorway. Laurel was standing at the window, arms folded, looking out. Krista was still reading to Flint. Jonathan had fallen asleep on the bed.

"Laurel, may I have a word with you?"

Laurel turned. "Sure."

Brynn took her into Flint's office and shut the door. Laurel said, "What's up?"

"Everything," Brynn replied. "First, how much longer are you going to stay?"

Laurel shrugged. "I don't know. I guess until I've paid back what I can for causing the accident. Why?"

"Because you're interfering in my relationship with Flint."

Laurel blinked. "What relationship?"

Brynn explained briefly, concluding, "It's serious and I'm not going to let it fall apart over you."

Laurel looked taken aback. "Brynn, what's gotten into you?"

"A strong sense of my own personal value," Brynn replied. "I love Flint and I'm growing certain that he loves me. I want you to stop pursuing him as a quick fix to your problems with Cord."

"And do what instead?"

"Solve your marital problems or divorce Cord. Your future isn't here."

"Brynn, you've made this mistake before, thinking Flint loves you. It chewed you up and spit you out."

Brynn shook her head. "There's far less danger of that now than there was five years ago. I've finally found myself, and I've found where I belong, too. Not in San Francisco, but here with Flint."

Laurel was silent for several moments, looking somewhat stunned and uncertain. Finally she said, "You may be right. Whenever I go in to him, he looks disappointed that it's me. He seems to know before I even say a word."

Brynn noticed Laurel's expression changing, relaxing. To Brynn's surprise, Laurel was starting to look relieved at being told to butt out.

"I think I'm right this time, Laurel."

"Well, maybe it's all for the best," Laurel said with a sigh. "Flint isn't the same since he went blind."

Brynn perceived, and sadly so, that Flint's blindness diminished him in Laurel's eyes. Laurel undoubtedly regretted being responsible for his injuries, and had done her best to atone, but it wasn't in her nature to love a blind man.

"What will you do if he ends up still blind, Brynn?"

Brynn didn't even have to think before replying, "I'll be his eyes."

Laurel shook her head. "I couldn't." She reached out and clasped Brynn's hand. "I hope he loves you, Brynn. You deserve it."

Brynn squeezed Laurel's fingers. "I know I have his love now. And he has mine."

"Well, then," said Laurel, brightening, "I'd better round up my brats and beat it back to Boise." She held out her arms to Brynn for a hug. "No hard feelings?"

Brynn hugged her twin tightly. "None at all. God bless and Godspeed."

Later, after Laurel gathered up the children and left, Brynn went to Flint's room. She paused in the doorway.

Flint turned sightless eyes to her. "Who's that?"

Silent, she waited.

Then he smiled, lighting her heart, saying, "Brynn. It's Brynn."

He put out a hand to her and she went to him. "Yes," she murmured. "Me." Placing her hand in his, she sat on the edge of the bed.

"Brynn," he said, and sighed. A solid statement of fact. A blind recognition.

"How can you tell?"

He guided her hand to his heart. "I've started seeing from here instead of through my eyes."

"Oh, Flint." Her eyes filled with tears of joy as she pressed a soft kiss to his lips. "I love you so much."

Flint took her into his arms and pillowed her head on his chest. "Thank God, Brynn. I need your love so much."

"Are you sure? Very sure?"

"To the last degree," he confirmed. "When my heart sees Laurel, it shrugs. But when it sees you, Brynn, it jumps with joy. When that started happening, I knew for sure and forever that I love you, yourself."

"Before that happened, you weren't certain?"

"Almost, but not quite. You weren't entirely sure, either, Brynn. Laurel made us both question ourselves and each other."

Brynn thought about that, then agreed. "Our uncertainties worked against us."

"We've got a different uncertainty now, Brynn. My eyesight. If it never comes back . . ."

"Shh." Brynn slipped under the covers with him and held him as close as she could without hurting his back. "Whatever happens, I'm with you every step of the way. One step at a time. One day at a time."

He gave a throaty, heartfelt sigh. "Together." His lips sought hers in a long, loving kiss. "Will you marry me, Brynn? For better or worse?"

She saw a sheen of tears in his blue eyes. "I will, Flint."

He smiled. "When?"

"June. Here in our home."

"You'll be my bride again."

"Your secondhand bride," she lovingly corrected.

Flint took up Brynn's left hand and tenderly kissed her ring finger. "The third time's the charm the way *I* count, Mrs. Wilder."

There was a sound in the doorway and Flint said, "Who's that?"

Wouldn't you know it was their own little Matchmaker.

Epilogue

FIVE MONTHS LATER, Brynn and Flint's dearly beloved gathered together in the great room at Wilder Butte Ranch to celebrate their union in holy matrimony.

The radiant bride wore a white silk wedding gown and a Spanish lace veil. The groom wore a tux and a Stetson—and glasses to aid his recovering eyesight. The wedding was the only one in anyone's experience that included a pet deer at the occasion.

Krista and Jonathan Hayden were flower girl and ring bearer; the best man was Roper Slocum. "The Wedding March" was to be played on twin pianos by the Mesdames Newton and Lyell.

Moments before the ceremony began, Brynn and her matron of honor, Laurel, put last-minute touches to their hair and makeup in the dressing room mirror.

"You look heavenly," Laurel said, adjusting Brynn's veil. "Simply stunning."

"And so do you," Brynn rejoined. "Have you and Dustin started dating seriously yet?"

Laurel nodded. "We're talking about an engagement, as soon as I'm legally free again. I can't believe I'm so helplessly in love with a nice conservative guy.

Where would I be now if he hadn't tracked me down in Boise?"

"I can't think of a more wonderful partner for my twin sister," Brynn said. "Loving the right man has changed you."

"For the better, in every way," Laurel agreed.

They smiled at each other in the mirror, eyes sparkling, cheeks pink with excitement, hearts full of love for each other and the men in their lives. The right men, at the right time.

At that moment, their mother came in, tearful with joy, and enfolded them both in a mother-bear hug. "My babies. I'm so happily ever after." She held them at arm's length, admiring them. "Ready, Brynn?"

"Yes!"

Maggie stepped out and signaled to Arch that Brynn was ready to be given away.

AND A SHORT TIME LATER, as Brynn and Flint stood united, making vows to love and cherish from this day forward, Constanza Rios sighed with utter and complete contentment.

It was so romantic. And so very true that love is repaid with love.

MILLS & BOON

CHRISTMAS CRACKERS

A cracker of a gift pack full of Mills & Boon goodies. You'll find...

Passion—in *A Savage Betrayal* by Lynne Graham

A beautiful baby—in *A Baby for Christmas* by Anne McAllister

A Yuletide wedding—in *Yuletide Bride* by Mary Lyons

A Christmas reunion—in *Christmas Angel* by Shannon Waverly

Special Christmas price of 4 books for £5.99 (usual price £7.96)

Published: November 1995

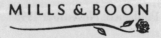

This month's
irresistible novels from

Temptation

IN PRAISE OF YOUNGER MEN by Lyn Ellis

Will Case was too big, far too attractive and much, much too sexy. And for the next few months, he would be sharing a cabin with Carolina. Will was also best friends with her little brother—and the same age!

THE RELUCTANT HUNK by Lorna Michaels

Ariel Foster wanted Jeff McBride to do a series for her TV station. She knew every woman in town would tune in to watch the drop-dead gorgeous man, if only she could persuade him to work for her. But she soon realised she wanted the reluctant hunk for herself.

BACHELOR HUSBAND by Kate Hoffmann

Come live and love in L.A. with the tenants of Bachelors Arms. The first in a captivating new mini-series.

Tru Hallihan lives in this trendy apartment block and has no thoughts of settling down. But he can't resist a bet to date popular radio presenter, Caroline Leighton. Caroline will only co-operate at a price—Tru must pose as her husband for a day!

SECOND-HAND BRIDE by Roseanne Williams

Brynn had married Flint Wilder knowing he was on the rebound from her twin sister, Laurel. Six months later, Brynn had left Flint, fearing she'd never be more than a substitute for her twin. Now Brynn was back in town and Flint seemed hell-bent on making up. But could she ever be sure she wasn't just a stand-in for her sister?

Spoil yourself next month
with these four novels from

Temptation

THE TWELVE GIFTS OF CHRISTMAS
by Rita Clay Estrada

Pete Cade might be the hunk every woman dreams of finding under her tree, but he wasn't ready to give the special gift at the top of Carly Michaels's Christmas list—a father for her daughter.

THE STRONG SILENT TYPE by Kate Hoffmann

Come live and love in L.A. with the tenants of Bachelors Arms. Second in a captivating mini-series.

Strong and silent Josh Banks had never been the subject of gossip before. But suddenly everyone was warning him about wild women—ever since he'd promised to keep party girl Taryn Wilde out of trouble. He could handle her…couldn't he?

FANCY-FREE by Carrie Alexander

Some residents don't approve of newcomer Fancy O'Brien taking a bath—in town—to publicize the opening of her bath boutique. But Jeremiah Quick is glad Fancy has arrived. He thinks Fancy's the right woman for him. Too bad *Fancy* thinks he's the right man for her mother…

BARGAIN BASEMENT BABY by Leandra Logan

Marriage had never appealed to Greg Baron. But since he was going to be a father, he didn't have much choice. If only the Baron family wasn't so thrilled to finally have an heir. If only his image of Jane Haley pregnant wasn't so delectable…

GET 4 BOOKS
AND A MYSTERY GIFT

Return this coupon and we'll send you 4 Temptations and a mystery gift absolutely FREE! We'll even pay the postage and packing for you.

We're making you this offer to introduce you to the benefits of Reader Service: FREE home delivery of brand-new Temptations, at least a month before they are available in the shops, FREE gifts and a monthly Newsletter packed with information.

Accepting these FREE books and gift places you under no obligation to buy, you may cancel at any time, even after receiving just your free shipment. Simply complete the coupon below and send it to:

MILLS & BOON READER SERVICE, FREEPOST, CROYDON, SURREY, CR9 3WZ.

No stamp needed

Yes, please send me 4 free Temptations and a mystery gift. I understand that unless you hear from me, I will receive 4 superb new titles every month for just £1.99* each postage and packing free. I am under no obligation to purchase any books and I may cancel or suspend my subscription at any time, but the free books and gifts will be mine to keep in any case. (I am over 18 years of age)

2EP5T

Ms/Mrs/Miss/Mr _____

Address _____

_____

_____ Postcode _____